SYNCHROTRON RADIATION IN MATERIALS SCIENCE

To learn more about AIP Conference Proceedings, including the
Conference Proceedings Series, please visit the webpage
http://proceedings.aip.org/proceedings

SYNCHROTRON RADIATION IN MATERIALS SCIENCE

6th International Conference on Synchrotron Radiation in Materials Science

Campinas, São Paulo, Brazil   20 – 23 July 2008

EDITOR
Rogério Magalhaes Paniago
Universidade Federal de Minas Gerais
Belo Horizonte, Brazil

SPONSORING ORGANIZATIONS
CNPQ - Conselho Nacional de Desenvolvimento Científico e Tecnológico
CAPES - Coordenação de Aperfeiçoamento de Pessoal de Nível Superior
PROSUL - Programa Sul-Americano de Apoio às Atividades de Cooperação em
    Ciência e Tecnologia
FAPESP - Fundação de Amparo à Pesquisa do Estado de São Paulo

Melville, New York, 2009
AIP CONFERENCE PROCEEDINGS ■ VOLUME 1092

Editor:

Prof. Dr. Rogério Magalhaes Paniago
Departamento de Física
Universidade Federal de Minas Gerais
CP 702, Belo Horizonte
Cep 30123-970 MG
Brazil

E-mail: paniago@lnls.br

L.C. Catalog Card No. 2008943585
ISBN 978-0-7354-0625-4
ISSN 0094-243X
Printed in the United States of America

CONTENTS

PREFACE

The Sixth International Conference on Synchrotron Radiation in Materials Science (SRMS-6) was held in Campinas, Brazil, from the 20th to the 23rd of July, 2008. The International Series of Meetings on Synchrotron Radiation in Materials Science brings together leading edge researchers from around the world and is a celebration of the increasingly important relationship between materials science and synchrotron radiation research. Special attention is given to the contribution that Synchrotron Radiation techniques have given to unsolved problems in Materials Science. This conference series started from the European Conference, SRMS-0, which was hosted by the Synchrotron Radiation Source, Daresbury Laboratory, UK in 1994. Later editions were held in 1996 (Illinois Institute of Technology, USA), 1998 (SPring8, Japan), 2001 (SSLS, Singapore), 2003 (ESRF, Grenoble, France) and 2006 (APS, Chicago, USA).

SRMS-6 was organized by the Brazilian Synchrotron Light Laboratory (LNLS, Campinas, SP). Several areas of SR research and Materials Science were encompassed, notably, Archaeological Materials, Catalysts and clusters, Complex oxides, Data-storage and Engineering materials, Films, Surfaces and Interfaces, Geo-physical and Electronic materials, Glasses and Ceramics, Liquids, Magnetism, Materials under Extreme conditions, Metals and Alloys, Metamaterials, Molecular electronics, Multiferroics, Nanostructured materials and Self-assembly, Polymers and Biomaterials, Photo materials, Nanofocus techniques, Strongly correlated materials, Superconducting materials, Industrial use of SR and Instrumentation/Recent Developments. Whilst the diversity of traditional areas at SRMS-6 was less than at previous SRMS meetings, Heritage, Nanomaterials, and Engineering Materials, for example, were now more strongly represented. For future meetings themes like Energy and Health are expected to come to the fore.

In total 40 invited talks, 30 oral contributions and 104 posters were presented at the conference. The papers published here represent the ongoing research of the participants, rather than work already published elsewere. We hope that these proceedings will provide an opportunity for many researchers who are involved with synchrotron radiation and materials science to share new ideas and concepts in this field.

We would like to thank the members of the International Advisory Committee for providing guidance on the scope of the conference and extensive suggestions of invited speakers. We also thank the authors who have contributed to the proceedings. The work of the Local Organizing Committee, especialy Mrs. Ana Ferreira, is gratefully acknowledged. We are thankful to the sponsors for supporting the conference. We also want to thank the staff members of AIP proceeding series, most notably Maya Flikop and Mary Waters, for help in producing this material.

Campinas, the 27th of November, 2008.

Rogério Magalhães Paniago

Departamento de Física, Universidade Federal de Minas Gerais
and Laboratorio Nacional de Luz Síncrotron

Molecular electronics studies by synchrotron radiation

Andrew T S Wee*, Wei Chen, Dongchen Chi, Shi Chen, Li Wang, Xingyu Gao

Department of Physics, National University of Singapore, 2 Science Drive 3, Singapore 117542
e-mail correspondence: phyweets@nus.edu.sg

Abstract. In molecular electronics research, the molecule-metal interfacial properties crucially control the electronic properties of the devices fabricated. We use synchrotron radiation techniques of PES and NEXAFS, complemented by STM, to study the molecular orientation and interfacial charge transfer processes of model molecule-metal systems.

Keywords: Molecular electronics, synchrotron, PES, NEXAFS, STM
PACS: 68.37.Ef, 79.60.Jv, 79.60.Fr

INTRODUCTION

The creation of well-ordered functional molecular arrays is one possible route towards the development for future molecular devices and biosensors. We have used synchrotron radiation techniques of photoelectron spectroscopy (PES) and near-edge x-ray absorption fine structure (NEXAFS), complemented by scanning tunneling microscopy (STM), to study the molecular orientation and interfacial charge transfer processes on surfaces. The synchrotron experiments were performed at the SINS beamline of the Singapore Synchrotron Light Source [1].

RESULTS AND CONCLUSIONS

We have elucidated the molecular orientation of 3,4,9,10-perylene-tetracarboxylic-dianhydride thin films at organic heterojunction interfaces [2]. *In situ* low-temperature STM and NEXAFS measurements (Fig. 1) were used to investigate the molecular orientation at the interface of PTCDA on copper(II) phthalocyanine (CuPc). On the CuPc monolayer on highly oriented pyrolitic graphite (HOPG), PTCDA molecules form a well-ordered in-plane herringbone structure with their molecular plane parallel to the substrate surface. The formation of multiple in-plane hydrogen bonding between neighboring PTCDA molecules is responsible for the flat-lying PTCDA on CuPc monolayer, and gives rise to the lying-down orientation of PTCDA thin films on both

CP1092, *Synchrotron Radiation in Materials Science: 6th International Conference*, edited by R. Magalhaes-Paniago
© 2009 American Institute of Physics 978-0-7354-0625-4/09/$25.00

standing-up and lying-down CuPc thin films, as well as on Au(111) passivated by a self-assembled monolayer of octane-1-thiol.

The conformation degree and molecular orientation during the growth of rubrene films on Si(111) and Au(111) have been studied by *in situ* x-ray absorption spectroscopy [3]. The backbones of rubrene molecules on Au(111) are twisted at the first few layers; in contrast, no appreciable twisting is observed on Si(111) even at a thickness of approximately 1.5 nm. The planarization of the backbone in the first few layers is due to strong molecule–substrate interactions between rubrene and Si(111). The rubrene molecules on Au(111) have a backbone tilt angle of 41° and a phenyl side group tilt of 64° with respect to the substrate surface, suggesting the crystalline nature of the films.

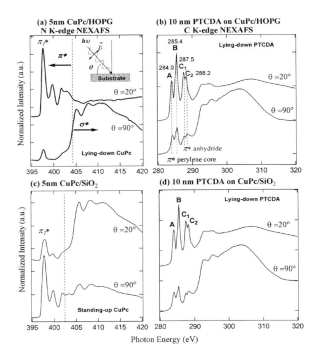

Figure 1 – Angle-dependent N K-edge NEXAFS spectra for the 5 nm CuPc on (a) HOPG and (c) SiO2 substrates, and C K-edge NEXAFS spectra after deposition of 10 nm PTCDA on (b) CuPc/HOPG and (d) CuPc/SiO2.

We have investigated the adsorption behavior of CuPc on Si(111) and the substrate effect on the valence state of the Cu atoms in CuPc by PES and NEXAFS [4]. The monolayer of CuPc on Si(111) is disordered, in contrast to the ordered multilayer CuPc. The formation of Si–C and Si–N bonds at the interface is clearly observed in the Si 2p and C 1s core level spectra. For the CuPc monolayer, the valence state for a portion of Cu atoms is reduced from 2+ to 1+. Further post-annealing significantly enhances the formation of Si–C and Si–N bonds between the molecules and the substrate, but the Cu 2p core level spectra reveal that the Cu valence state remains unchanged. This suggests that the Cu atoms are well shielded from the surrounding environment by the distortion of the CuPc molecules.

Controlling charge doping in organic semiconductors represents one of the key challenges in organic electronics. Charge transfer or charge separation at the molecule/substrate interface can be used to dope the semiconductor surface or the active molecular layers close to the interface, and this process is referred to as surface-transfer doping. We have investigated the surface transfer doping of organic semiconductors using functionalized self-assembled monolayers [5]. By modifying the Au(111) substrate with self-assembled monolayers (SAMs) of aromatic thiols with strong electron-withdrawing trifluoromethyl (CF_3) functional groups, significant electron transfer from the active organic layers (copper(II) phthalocyanine; CuPc) to the underlying CF_3-SAM near the interface is clearly observed by synchrotron photoemission spectroscopy. The electron transfer at the CuPc/CF3-SAM interface leads to an electron accumulation layer in CF3-SAM and a depletion layer in CuPc, thereby achieving p-type doping of the CuPc layers close to the interface. In contrast, methyl (CH_3)-terminated SAMs do not display significant electron transfer behavior at the CuPc/CH3-SAM interface, suggesting that these effects can be generalized to other organic-SAM interfaces.

We have also performed surface transfer doping of diamond(100) by tetrafluoro-tetracyanoquino-dimethane [6], as well as on epitaxial graphene by tetrafluoro-tetracyanoquino-dimethane (F4-TCNQ). [7]. Epitaxial graphene thermally grown on 6H-SiC(0001) (Fig. 2) can be p-type doped via a novel surface transfer doping scheme by modifying the surface with the electron acceptor F4-TCNQ. Synchrotron-based high-resolution PES reveals that electron transfer from graphene to adsorbed F4-TCNQ is responsible for the p-type doping of graphene. This novel surface transfer doping scheme by surface modification with appropriate molecular acceptors represents a simple and effective method to nondestructively dope epitaxial graphene for future nanoelectronics applications.

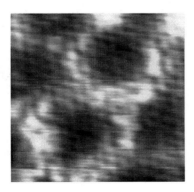

Figure 2 – 4×4 nm^2 STM image of epitaxial graphene thermally grown on SiC(0001)

We have used resonant photoemission to study electron transfer at the molecule-metal interface of self-assembled monolayers of 1,1';4',1''-terphenyl-4''-thiol (BBB) and its partially fluorinated counterpart (BFF: p-thiophenyl-nonafluorobiphenyl) on Au(111) [8]. Our approach has been rfered to as core-hole clock spectroscopy, which allows us to probe ultrafast electron transfer at the BBB/Au(111) interface in the low-femtosecond regime (on the same time scale as the C 1s core-hole lifetime of 6 fs). In contrast, for BFF/Au(111), the interface electron transfer was forbidden during the corehole decay. This strongly suggests that fluorination of phenyl rings significantly enhances the localization of the excited electrons in the LUMO.

CONCLUSION

We have used synchrotron radiation techniques of PES and NEXAFS, complemented by STM, to study the molecular orientation and interfacial charge transfer processes on surface and interfaces. Such studies help us understand the interfacial electronic processes at organic-organic and organic-inorganic interfaces which have potential applications in organic electronics.

REFERENCES

1. X. J. Yu, O. Wilhelmi, H. O. Moser, S. V. Vidyaraj, X. Y. Gao, A. T. S. Wee, T. Nyunt, H. J. Qian, H. W. Zheng, *J. Elec. Spectrosc. Related Phenom.* 2005, *144*, 1031.
2. W. Chen; H. Huang; S. Chen; L. Chen, H. L. Zhang; X. Y. Gao; A. T. S. Wee; *Appl. Phys. Lett.* 2007, *91*, 114102.
3. L. Wang; S. Chen; L. Liu; D. C. Qi; X. Y. Gao; J. Subbiah; S. Swaminathan; A. T. S. Wee; *J. Appl. Phys.* 2007, *102*, 063504.
4. L. Wang; S. Chen; D. C. Qi; X. Y. Gao; A. T. S. Wee, *Surf. Sci.* 2007, *601*, 4212.
5. W. Chen; X. Y. Gao; D. C. Qi; S. Chen; Z. K. Chen; A. T. S. Wee; *Adv. Func Mat.* 2007, *17*, 1339.
6. D. Qi; W. Chen; X. Gao; L. Wang; S. Chen; K. P. Loh; A. T. S. Wee; *J. Am. Chem. Soc.* 2007, *129*, 8084.
7. W. Chen; S. Chen; D. C. Qi; X. Y. Gao; A. T. S. Wee; *J. Am. Chem. Soc.* 2007, *129*, 10418.
8. W. Chen; L. Wang; C. Huang; T. T. Lin; X. Y. Gao; K. P. Loh; Z. K. Chen; A. T. S. Wee; *J. Am. Chem. Soc.* 2006, *128*, 935.

Transitions in network and molecular glasses at high pressure.

Chris J. Benmore[1,2,*], Emmanuel Soignard[2], Qiang Mei[3], Sabyasachi Sen[4], John B. Parise[5] and Jeffery L. Yarger[2].

1. X-ray Science Division, Argonne National Laboratory, Argonne IL 60439, USA
benmore@anl.gov
2. Arizona State University, Department of Chemistry and Biochemistry, Department of Physics
esoignar@usa.net, jeff.yarger@asu.edu, chris.benmore@asu.edu
3. HPCAT, Geophysical Laboratory, Carnegie Institution of Washington, Argonne National
Laboratory, Argonne, IL 60439, USA
Qiang.mei@hpcat.aps.anl.gov
4. University of California at Davis, Department of Materials Science
sbsen@ucdavis.edu
5. State University of New York, Department of Geosciences
John.parise@sunysb.edu

Abstract. The use of monochromatic, micro-focused, high energy x-ray beams have been used in combination with perforated diamond anvil cells to investigate transitions in several network glasses at high pressure. Of particular interest are glasses which readily form an open network structure e.g. SiO_2, $GeSe_2$, BeF_2 and those which comprise of small molecular cages e.g. As_4S_3, As_4O_6. These materials have highly directional bonds and their normal pressure glassy forms tend to have a high degree of intermediate range order, signified by the existence of a first sharp diffraction peak. As the pressure is increased this peak decreases dramatically in intensity as the open regions of the network collapse. Simultaneously the (second) principal peak increases in intensity as the molecules in the glass move closer together resulting in increased extended range order. Gradual and abrupt amorphous-amorphous transitions have been observed in these binary systems, associated with both topological and local coordination number changes.

Keywords: Glasses, x-ray diffraction, high pressure
PACS: 61.43.Fs, 61.05.cp, 81.40.Vw

INTRODUCTION

The investigation of high pressure liquid-liquid or amorphous-amorphous transitions represents a topical and growing field in synchrotron materials research. However the study of disordered materials at high pressure presents several technical challenges; the sample signal is inherently weak due to the disordered nature of the material, the background is high due to the large cell assembly required to generate the pressure, and a measurement over a wide momentum transfer range is required to provide good real space resolution. Nonetheless, advances in high energy x-ray

CP1092, *Synchrotron Radiation in Materials Science: 6th International Conference*, edited by R. Magalhaes-Paniago
© 2009 American Institute of Physics 978-0-7354-0625-4/09/$25.00

focusing optics now enable high pressure experiments on glasses and liquids using diamond anvil cells (DACs), allowing a wide range of pressures to be explored. The high energy x-ray measurements are perfomed in transmission geometry using large area detectors to ensure good statistics over a wide momentum transfer range. The Compton scattering from the diamonds, which can commonly dominate the signal at high Q, has also been aliviated to some extent by the use of mechanically or laser perforated diamond anvils, enabling the measurement of samples containing lighter elements.

RESULTS AND DISCUSSION

We have studied a range of binary network and molecular glasses at high pressure using this technique to identify transitions in the amorphous state using beamline 1-ID at the Advanced Photon Source. Examples of diffraction patterns taken on chalcogenide and oxide glasses either side of a transition are shown in figure 1. The most noticeable changes in the measured structure factor, S(Q), occur in the low-Q region.

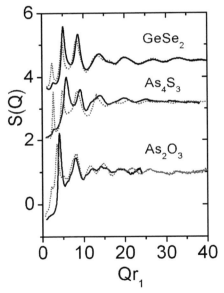

Figure 1 – X-ray structure factors of some binary glasses before (red, dotted line) at normal pressure and after a transition (black, solid line) at high pressure. The quantity r_1 represents the position of the first peak in the radial distribution function for the normal pressure measurement. The high pressure S(Q) for $GeSe_2$ was measured at 5.3 GPa; As_4S_3 at 13.7 GPa; As_2O_3 at 32 GPa.

There have been several interpretations of the first sharp diffraction peak in network glasses, which is typically located at $Qr_1 \sim 2.5$ in the S(Q) diffraction pattern, but there is general acceptance that it is associated with intermediate range order which can extend out to several molecular units in length [1]. The reduction in intensity with pressure represents a breakdown of this network. Similarly, the increase in intensity of the principal (second) peak with increasing pressure has been associated with increased extended range order due to the closer packing of units within the glass [2].

Amorphous-amorphous transitions have been previously reported in GeO_2 [3], $GeSe_2$ [4,5] and As_4S_3 [6,7] using high energy x-ray diffraction. In addition, transitions have also been observed in As_2O_3 [8,9] and BeF_2 [10]. An outline of the results is presented in table 1. The well known transition from a tetrahedral to octahedral network in vitreous GeO_2 occurs via an intermediate high pressure form in which the average Ge coordination number is ~5 [3]. In contrast, the transition in glassy As_2O_3 has been associated with a jump from AsO_3 to AsO_6 units, with no evidence of the formation of intermediate AsO_4 polyehdra [9].

Glassy Network or molecule	Dominant unit at normal pressure	Possible high pressure form
SiO_2, GeO_2 Corner shared tetrahedra		Octahedral network
BeF_2 Corner shared tetrahedra		Topological transition ?
$GeSe_2$ Edge and corner shared tetrahedra		Corner shared tetrahedra & coordination change
As_4O_6 molecule		AsO_6 network
As_4S_3 molecule		High density network

Table 1 – Binary network glasses studied at high pressure using high energy x-ray diffraction at the Advanced Photon Source.

In chalcogenide glasses transitions can be much more difficult to identify using a single diffraction measurement due to formation of homopolar bonds. In $GeSe_2$ glass, for example, there are two competing densification mechanisms; a gradual increase in coordination number and a conversion from edge to corner shared tetrahedra [4]. A gradual transition is reflected by a minimum in the shear velocity, indicating a minimum also occurs in the network rigidity with pressure [5]. The collapse of zero dimensional molecular molecules such as As_4S_3 however can be readily identified by changes in the local structure, and the growth of a high density network has been identified at longer distances [6].

CONCLUSION

The investigation of transitions in glasses and liquids at high pressure is still in its' infancy. The structural rearrangements during the transitions are often unpredictable, since the local bonding and connectivity of units can often be different from that found in the crystalline state. Given the technical and theoretical hurdles needed to make progress in this field, information from a variety of spectroscopic, thermodynamic and diffraction techniques are required to obtain a coherent picture of these high pressure glasses. However, recent advances in micro-focussed high energy x-ray optics, the use of large area detectors and perforated diamond anvil cells is starting to provide a valuable insight into the behaviour of these materials with pressure.

ACKNOWLEDGEMENTS

This work was supported by Argonne National Laboratory under contract number DE-AC02-06CH11357, NSF chemistry and by the Carnegie/DOE Alliance Center (DOE-NNSA CDAC) CDAC (JLY), NSF grant DMR 0603933 (SS), the U.S. DOE EAR-0510501, NSF DMR-0452444, DOD and the Keck Foundation (JBP).

REFERENCES

1. Q. Mei, C.J. Benmore, S. Sen, R. Sharma and J.L. Yarger. *Phys. Rev. B 78* (2008) 144204.
2. Salmon, P. S., Martin, R. A., Mason, P. E. & Cuello, G. J. *Nature* 2005, *435*, 75.
3. M. Guthrie, C.A. Tulk, C.J. Benmore, J. Xu, J.L. Yarger H-K. Mao and R.J. Hemley. *Phys. Rev. Lett.* 2004, *93*, 115502.
4. Q. Mei, C.J. Benmore, R.T. Hart, E. Bychkov, P.S. Salmon, C.D. Martin, F.M. Michel, S.M. Antao, P.J. Chupas, P.L. Lee, S.D. Shastri, J.B. Parise, K. Leinenweber, S. Amin and J.L. Yarger. *Phys. Rev. B.,* 2006, *74*, 014203.
5. S.M. Antao, C.J. Benmore, B. Li, L. Wang, E. Bychkov and J.B. Parise. Submitted to Phys. Rev.
6. S. Sen, S. Gaudio, B. G. Aitken, and C. E. Lesher. *Phys. Rev. Lett.,* 2006, *97*, 025506.
7. S. Soyer Uzun, S. J. Gaudio, S. Sen, Q. Mei, C.J. Benmore, C.A. Tulk, J. Xu. *J. Phys. Chem. Solids,* accepted.
8. Q. Mei, C.J. Benmore, E. Soignard, S. Amin, J.L. Yarger. *J. Phys.: Condens. Matter,* 2007, *19*, 415103.
9. E. Soignard, S. Amin, Q. Mei, C.J. Benmore, J.L. Yarger. Submitted to *Phys. Rev B.*
10. E. Soignard *et al,* in preparation.

Surface x-ray diffraction of complex metal oxide surfaces and interfaces – a new era

C.M. Schlepütz[1], P.R. Willmott[*1], S.A. Pauli[1], R. Herger[1], D. Martoccia[1], M. Björck[1], D. Kumah[2], R. Clarke[2], and Y. Yacoby[3]

[1]Swiss Light Source, Paul Scherrer Institut, CH-5232 Villigen, Switzerland.
[2]Randall Laboratory of Physics and FOCUS Center, University of Michigan, Ann Arbor, Michigan, 48109-1120, USA.
[3]Racah Institute of Physics, Hebrew University, Jerusalem, 91904, Israel.
philip.willmott@psi.ch, stephan.pauli@psi.ch, christian.schlepuetz@psi.ch, roger.herger@accenture.com, domenico.martoccia@psi.ch, matts.bjorck@psi.ch, dkumah@umich.edu, royc@umich.edu, yizhak@vms.huji.ac.il

Abstract. The availability of high-brilliance hard x-ray synchrotron radiation and the advent of novel photon counting area detectors have brought surface x-ray diffraction (SXRD) into a new era. It is now possible to record large numbers of structure factors with much improved reliability within reasonable beamtime durations. As a result, structural determination of the surfaces and interfaces of complex crystallographic systems and heterostructures has now become feasible, especially in conjunction with phase-retrieval methods. It is thereby hoped that detailed structural information will shed light on the unusual physical properties of these systems. Complex metal oxide systems investigated at the Materials Science beamline of the Swiss Light Source, including the surface of $SrTiO_3$, the interface between $LaAlO_3$ and $SrTiO_3$, and the structure of $YBa_2Cu_3O_7$ grown on $NdGaO_3$, $SrTiO_3$, and $(LaSr)(AlTa)O_3$ will be presented as examples of what is now possible using SXRD.

INTRODUCTION

Complex metal oxides, in particular the perovskite family, demonstrate an exceedingly broad range of electronic and magnetic properties, due principally to the complex interplay of the valence electrons in such systems. Subtle structural changes (e.g., in bond angles and bond lengths) can induce fundamental changes in the physics of these so-called strongly correlated electron systems (SCESs). It is therefore to be expected that at their surface regions and at heteroepitaxial interfaces, unusual phenomena can arise [1-3], which, on the one hand set a limit to the downsizing of devices exploiting their bulk properties, but on the other, might lead to novel physical properties not existing in their bulk counterparts.

CP1092, *Synchrotron Radiation in Materials Science: 6th International Conference*, edited by R. Magalhaes-Paniago

SURFACE X-RAY DIFFRACTION

Because structural changes of the order of a percent can be critical in SCESs in altering the balance between competing energetics, which in turn fundamentally influences the physical properties, a spatial resolution of a small fraction of an Angstrom is required in the structural determination of their surfaces and interfaces. Surface x-ray diffraction (SXRD) is unique in meeting this criterion [4].

In SXRD, the intensity of the diffracted signal is measured in between Bragg maxima in a direction perpendicular to the (atomically flat) surface (see Fig. 1). The signal strength depends sensitively on the positions of the atoms in the surface and/or interface region. For complex systems, such as those with which we are concerned here, a large number of structure factors must be recorded in order to obtain a reliable model.

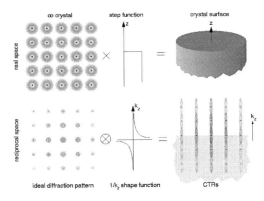

Figure 1 – The signal strength between Bragg peaks perpendicular to the surface is nonzero due to the convolution of a bulklike diffraction pattern with the shape function of an abrupt and flat surface. The exact form of this signal depends sensitively on the deviations of the surface (or interface) atoms from bulk positions.

PHASE-RETRIEVAL METHODS

Indeed, it is not unusual that in the case of SCESs, the positions of over one hundred atoms must be accurately determined to obtain the structure. Unsurprisingly, standard least-square minimization fitting methods normally fail to find the global minimum in such multi-parameter spaces unless the starting model very closely approximates reality.

A more promising approach seems to be phase-retrieval methods on strongly oversampled data sets, which are model-free [5]. An example of an electron density map extracted using the coherent Bragg rod analysis (COBRA) technique is shown in Fig. 2 [6].

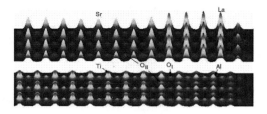

Figure 2 – Electron density maps of a five-monolayer thin film of $LaAlO_3$ grown heteroepitaxially on $SrTiO_3$, in planes perpendicular to the surface. The top map contains the SrO-LaO layers, while the bottom map contains the TiO_2-GaO_2 layers, as determined using the COBRA phase-retrieval method.

For these complex systems, one typically needs to record of the order of 10,000 structure factors to obtain sufficiently large data sets in order to perform phase-retrieval methods. This is impractical within typical beamtime allocation periods using conventional SXRD techniques using point detectors, even at third-generation synchrotron facilities. However, the employment of the novel photon-counting pixel x-ray detector PILATUS 100k has accelerated data acquisition rates by over an order of magnitude, while also improving the reliability of the extracted structure factors (see Fig. 3) [7].

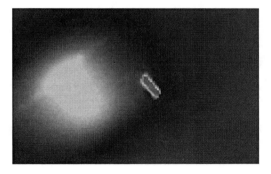

Figure 3 – An example of a crystal truncation rod signal (sharp feature in red) approaching a Bragg peak (broad signal in green) from the surface of $NdGaO_3$ (110), as recorded using the PILATUS 100k pixel detector.

EXAMPLES

In this contribution, SXRD methods are discussed and results are presented for several perovskite structures and interfaces, including, among others, the structure of 4.5 nm thick $YBa_2Cu_3O_7$ films on $NdGaO_3$, $SrTiO_3$, and $(LaSr)(AlTa)O_3$ substrates; the surface of $SrTiO_3$, as the prototypical substrate material for perovskite thin film growth [8]; and the conducting interface [6] of a five-monolayer $LaAlO_3$ film grown heteroepitaxially on $SrTiO_3$(001) by pulsed laser deposition.

11

REFERENCES

1. J. G. Bednorz; K.-A. Müller *Z. Phys. B* 1986 *64* 189.
2. S. Jin; T. H. Tiefel; M. McCormack; R. A. Fastnacht; R. Ramesh; L. H. Chen *Science* 1994, *264*, 413.
3. A. Ohtomo; H. Y. Hwang *Nature* 2004, *427*, 423.
4. R. Feidenhans'l *Surf. Sci. Rep.* 1989, *10*, 105.
5. Y. Yacoby; M. Sowwan; E. A. Stern; J. Cross; D. Brewe; R. Pindak; J. Pitney; E. B. Dufresne; R. Clarke *Physica* 2003, *336B*, 39.
6. P. R. Willmott; S. A. Pauli; R. Herger; C. M. Schlepütz; D. Martoccia; B. D. Patterson; B. Delley; R. Clarke; D. Kumah; C. Cionca; Y. Yacoby *Phys. Rev. Lett.* 2007, *99*, 155502.
7. C. M. Schlepütz; R. Herger; P. R. Willmott; B. D. Patterson; O. Bunk; C. Brönnimann; B. Henrich; G. Hülsen; E. F. Eikenberry *Acta Crystallogr. A* 2005, *61*, 418.
8. R. Herger; P. R. Willmott; O. Bunk; C. M. Schlepütz; B.D. Patterson: B. Delley *Phys. Rev. Lett.* 2007, *98*, 076102.

Charge excitations in high-T_c superconducting copper oxides studied by resonant inelastic x-ray scattering

Kenji Ishii*

*SPring-8, Japan Atomic Energy Agency, 1-1-1 Kouto, Sayo-cho, 679-5148 Hyogo, JAPAN.

Abstract. Momentum-dependent charge excitations in high-T_c superconducting copper oxides are investigated by resonant inelastic x-ray scattering at the Cu K-edge. An excitation across the Mott gap excitation is observed in parent materials and it shows a characteristic dispersion relation in the CuO_2 plane. The Mott gap excitation persists in carrier doped superconductors. When holes are doped, the dispersion becomes smaller, while the intensity of the Mott gap excitation concentrates at the Brillouin zone center upon electron doping. At the same time, an intraband excitation of doped carriers emerges below the gap in both hole- and electron-dope cases. The observed momentum dependence is consistent with a theoretical calculation based on a Hubbard model.

INTRODUCTION

Resonant inelastic x-ray scattering (RIXS) in the hard x-ray regime is a developing experiment technique to measure charge excitations by utilizing brilliant synchrotron radiation x-rays. It has a great advantage that the momentum dependence of electronic excitations can be measured unlike conventional optical method. In addition, RIXS gives element-selective excitation spectra by tuning the incident photon energy to an absorption edge of the element. There has been much activity in recent years using this technique, especially in strongly correlated transition metal oxides.

Here, I would like to present our RIXS studies on high-Tc superconductors and related materials which were performed in close collaboration with theorists. Parent materials of the high-Tc superconductors are Mott insulator, in which a charge gap, so-called Mott gap, exists due to the strong Coulomb repulsion between electrons. By carrier doping, the gap is filled and superconductivity emerges. Therefore evolution of the electronic structure upon carrier doping is an important issue in the strongly correlated electron systems and we investigated intensively the doping dependence of RIXS spectra.

CP1092, *Synchrotron Radiation in Materials Science: 6th International Conference*, edited by R. Magalhaes-Paniago
© 2009 American Institute of Physics 978-0-7354-0625-4/09/$25.00

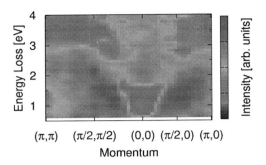

FIGURE 1. RIXS spectra of the electron-doped superconductor $Nd_{1.85}Ce_{0.15}CuO_4$.

Results and Discussion

In Nd_2CuO_4 and $YBa_2Cu_3O_6$, which are parent materials of high-T_c superconductors, Mott gap is clearly observed at the all momenta. An anisotropic dispersion in the CuO_2 plane, that is, larger dispersion along the $[\pi,\pi]$ direction than the $[\pi,0]$ direction, is commonly observed. The dispersion becomes smaller in the hole-doped superconductor $Ca_{1.8}Na_{0.2}CuO_2Br_2$. An intraband charge excitation of doped holes appears as continuum intensity below the gap. On the other hand, the Mott gap excitation is prominent at the Brillouin zone center in the electron-doped superconductor $Nd_{1.85}Ce_{0.15}CuO_4$. The intraband excitation of doped electrons is observed at finite momentum transfer and it shifts to higher energy with the increase of the peak width as a function of momentum transfer as shown in Fig. 1. Furthermore the dispersive intraband excitation is qualitatively similar to the dynamical charge correlation function $N(Q,\omega)$. These characteristics are consistent with calculated RIXS spectra using the numerically exact diagonalization technique on a small cluster of a Hubbard model.

SUMMARY

We have performed a Cu K-edge RIXS study of high-Tc cuprates from parent Mott insulators to carrier-doped superconductors. Interband excitation of the Mott gap and intraband excitation of doped carriers are investigated.

ACKNOWLEDGEMENT

The author would like to acknowledge to his collaborators, K. Tsutsui, Y. Endoh, T. Tohyama, T. Inami, M. Hoesch, J. Mizuki, Y. Murakami, S. Maekawa, T. Masui, S. Tajima, K. Yamada, H. Kawashima, and J. Akimitsu.

REFERENCES

1. K. Ishii et al., *Phys. Rev. Lett.* 2005, 94, 187002.

2. K. Ishii et al., *Phys. Rev. Lett.* 2005, 94, 207003.
3. K. Ishii et al., arXiv:0708.3534v1.

Applications of synchrotron-based micro-imaging techniques for the analysis of Cultural Heritage materials.

Marine Cotte*[1, 2], Javier Chilida[3], Philippe Walter[1], Yoko Taniguchi[4], Jean Susini[2]

1 Center of Research and Restoration of the French Museums, Palais du Louvre, Porte des Lions, 14 quai F. Mitterrand, 75001 Paris, FRANCE
2. European Synchrotron Radiation Facilit, BP220, 38043 Grenoble Cedex, France
3. Private curator, Barcelona, Spain.
4 JCICC- NRICP,Tokyo, 13-43, Ueno koen, Tokyo, 110-8713 Japan
cotte@esrf.fr, susini@esrf.fr, philippe.walter@culture.gouv.fr, taniguchi@tobunken.go.jp

Abstract. The analysis of cultural Heritage objects is often technically challenging. When analyzing micro-fragments, the amount of matter is usually very tiny, hence requiring sensitive techniques. These samples, in particular painting fragments, may present multi-layered structures, with layer thickness of ~10µm. It leads to favor micro-imaging techniques, with a good lateral resolution (about one micrometer), that manage the discriminative study of each layer. Besides, samples are usually very complex in term of chemistry, as they are made of mineral and organic matters, amorphous and crystallized phases, major and minor elements. Accordingly, a multi-modal approach is generally essential to solve the chemical complexity of such hybrid materials. Different examples will be given, to illustrate the various possibilities of synchrotron-based micro-imaging techniques, such as micro X-ray diffraction, micro X-ray fluorescence, micro X-ray absorption spectroscopy and micro FTIR spectroscopy. Focus will be made on paintings, but the whole range of museum objects (going from soft matter like paper or wood to hard matter like metal and glass) will be also considered.

Keywords: synchrotron, painting, imaging, FTIR, XANES, alteration, pigment.
PACS: 07.85.Qe

INTRODUCTION

The interest of the art and archaeology community for synchrotron radiation shows a recent intensification, as exemplified by the increasing number of dedicated workshops and conferences. The application of macro and micro-imaging techniques can be highly effective for the study of artworks. Ancient paintings are an extreme example due to their multi-layered arrangement, with layers of a few micrometers, and due to their chemical complexity (mixture of inorganic pigments and organic binders, crystallized and amorphous phases, major and minor elements).

CP1092, *Synchrotron Radiation in Materials Science: 6th International Conference*, edited by R. Magalhaes-Paniago
© 2009 American Institute of Physics 978-0-7354-0625-4/09/$25.00

Different recent examples will be given, which illustrate the two main preoccupations of curators and conservators: looking backwards, to get insight into ancient artistic practices; and looking forwards, to restore and preserve works of art as long as possible. They will exemplify some micro-imaging techniques available on synchrotron facilities.

RESULTS AND DISCUSSION

Two opposite methodological strategies can be followed for the study of paintings. On the one hand, analyses performed directly on the entire painting, without any sampling. On the other hand, when sampling is possible, the study of micro-fragments. These approaches face distinct and common technical challenges.

In the first case, non-invasiveness and depth of penetration are key points. In the second case, beam size is crucial, as the micrometric probe is necessary to perform a selective analysis of each painting layers. In the two cases, solving chemical complexity requires sensitive techniques.

The field of view of these two approaches is by nature opposite. Macro-imaging techniques such as tomography, laminography or K-edge imaging will offer a centrimetric vision of objects, while micro-analytical techniques, such as micro X-ray diffraction (μXRD), micro X-ray fluorescence (μXRF), micro Fourier Transform Infrared (μFTIR), micro X-ray absorption spectroscopy (μXAS) will usually be employed to focus on micrometric grains of pigments. Indeed, these two approaches (macro and micro) are intrinsically complementary and can be helpfully cross-linked.

As an example, macro X-ray fluorescence was used to reveal a lost portrait painted by Van Gogh.[1] Hopefully, this painting, which was hidden under a posterior patch of grass, was done with antimony pigment, a high-Z element whose fluorescence could be detected even across the 100μm over layers. In parallel, μXRF and μXANES were performed on a fragment for a better identification of the antimony pigment.

Here after are given two examples of analysis of micro fragments. In the first one, the work was motivated by the identification of organic binders in ancient Buddhist paintings. In the second case, focus is made on the better understanding of a pigment alteration.

LOOKING BACKWARDS: STUDY OF ANCIENT BUDDHIST PAINTINGS

Bamiyan, Foladi and Kakrak sites are located in the highlands of Afghanistan, in the middle of Bamiyan valley where Buddhism used to flourish between 5th and 9th centuries, as symbolized by two Giant Buddhas, magnificent Buddhist paintings in caves, temples and possibly a nirvana Buddha. About 50 caves still keep some but very few remaining portions of the mural paintings after the demolition by Talibans. The Bamiyan site was, therefore, inscribed in 2003 on the World Heritage in Danger List, and became subject to protection within an international cooperation. Since this project has been funded by the UNESCO-Japanese Funds-in-Trust, a Japanese institution, NRICP, was chosen to execute the conservation project, 'Safeguarding of the Bamiyan Site' within the framework of UNESCO.[2]

Aiming to set appropriate conservation strategies and to comprehend the painting techniques of the Bamiyan Mural Paintings, detailed technical studies for painting materials and studies for deterioration mechanisms are developed. Although the paintings represent Buddhist motifs and stories, their painting materials and techniques could have been strongly influenced by Mediterranean or West Asian regions through the trade in the ancient period. Chemical analyses are a good way to tackle any evidence of such both organic and inorganic material influences from various regions in a broader context. Recent experiments were conducted at the ESRF, in order to better identify these various ingredients. Analyses were performed on thin cross-sections by combining μXRD/μXRF (ID18F) and μFTIR (ID21). They reveal the presence of a wide set of compounds, with a high diversity not only of pigments but also of binders. They shed a new light on artistic practices used 15 centuries ago, in Bamiyan, a connection point East and West through the Eurasia Continent, at the middle of the Silk Road.[3-4]

LOOKING FORWARDS: BLACKENING OF SPANISH GOTHIC PAINTINGS

Mercury sulfide (HgS), commonly named cinnabar, is a deep red pigment, extensively used since the Antiquity. Yet, in certain circumstances, it can be unstable, turning into sad grey-black shades. This phenomenon is commonly explained as the phase transformation of red cinnabar into black meta-cinnabar by action of light. However, other mechanisms have been proposed recently. Different analyses were performed at the ID21-beamline (ESRF) to tackle this problem by micro X-ray fluorescence and micro X-ray absorption spectroscopy.

A first set of analyses was achieved on Pompeian wall paintings.[5] In this case, two alteration pathways were evidenced: the formation of black films, containing mainly gypsum; and the formation of grey alterations, containing chloride compounds.

A second set of studies was carried on Gothic paintings from the Pedralbes monastery (Barcelona, Spain).[4] Here again, chlorine was clearly involved in the degradation. Different steps of alteration were visualized thanks to chemical mappings. The original cinnabar turns first into mercury sulfide chloride, and then into mercury chlorides, without any sulfur. In this example, gothic paintings had been covered with an ulterior lime wash which was also evidenced by XANES (Fig. 1).

CONCLUSION

The unique advantages that synchrotron radiation offers, e.g., high brightness, small beam, wavelength tunability are highly rewarded for the micro-analysis of precious and complex samples. Imaging is crucial for the study of such structured and heterogeneous arrangements. Micrometer probes are essential for the discriminative study of each layer. Micro-FTIR is particularly useful for the identification and location of the different organic binders (fat, protein, gum...).[3-4,6] Micro X-ray diffraction is more adapted for the analysis of mineral compounds. Combined with micro X-ray fluorescence, it offers a powerful tool for the precise identification of pigments and plasters. The major advantage of micro X-ray absorption spectroscopy is the possibility to specifically study the chemical environment of a particular element, even in a complex mixture.[4-7] Finally, in addition to the common and distinct advantages of the different synchrotron based-techniques, the combination of all these micro-analytical tools provide a unique approach for the chemical analysis of art objects and paintings in particular.

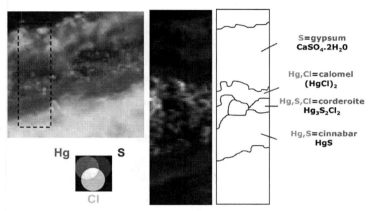

Figure 1 – Darkening of cinnabar (HgS) mural paintings from Pedralbes. Left; visible light picture of a painting cross-section showing, from bottom to top: white mortar, red cinnabar, grey alteration, white lime wash. Center: RGB elemental mappings obtained by micro-fluorescence. Right: sketch of the chemical distribution, according to μXANES studies at the chlorine and sulfur K-edges (map size: 60×18μm²).

REFERENCES

1. J. Dik, K. Janssens, G. van der Snickt, L. van der Loeff, K. Rickers and M. Cotte, *Anal. Chem.* 2008, *80* (16), 6436.
2. JCICC, 2004. Protecting the World Heritage Site of Bamiyan: Key Issues for the Establishment of a Comprehensive Management Plan 2004, NRICP, Japan.
3. Y. Taniguchi, M. Cotte, E. Checroun, H. Otake, *Science for conservation* 2007, *46*, 181.
4. M. Cotte, J. Susini, V. A. Solé, Y. Taniguchi, J. Chillida, E. Checroun, P. Walter, *JAAS* 2008, *23*, 820.
5. M. Cotte, J. Susini, A. Moscato, C. Gratziu, A. Bertagnini, N. Metrich, *Anal. Chem.* 2006, *78*, 7484.
6. V. Mazel , P. Richardin, D. Debois, D. Touboul, M. Cotte, A. Brunelle, P. Walter, O. Laprévote, *Anal. Chem* 2007, *79*, 9253.
7. M. Cotte, E. Welcomme, V.A. Solé, M. Salomé, M. Menu, Ph. Walter, J. Susini, *Anal. Chem* 2007, *79*, 6988.

Pressure induced amorphisation and the amorphous-amorphous transition in nano-TiO₂: An X-ray Absorption Spectroscopy study.

A -M. Flank[1]*, P. Lagarde[1], J-P. Itié[1], A. Polian[2], G.R. Hearne[3]

1. SOLEIL Synchrotron, L'Orme des Merisiers, BP 48, F-91192 GIF/Yvette, France
2. Physique des Milieux Denses, IMPMC, CNRS, Université Pierre et Marie Curie -Paris 6,
140 rue de Lourmel, 75015 Paris, France
3. School of Physics & DST-NRF CoE in Strong Materials, WITS University, Johannesburg, South Africa

Abstract. The novel phenomenon of grain-size dependent pressure induced amorphisation (PIA) in TiO₂ nano-materials has been evidenced by several experiments in recent years. The open questions of the structural details of the high density amorphous (HDA) phase have been addressed in a x-ray absorption spectroscopy (XAS) pressure study at the Ti K-edge. The local environment of the cation, to within a few nearest neighbor shells, has been monitored up to ~30 GPa where the HDA phase is stabilised. The XAS investigations of this study suggest that a precursor phase is observed before amorphization, the nature of which depends on the experimental conditions. A new structure is stabilized in all cases of samples decompressed from the HDA phase to ambient conditions, characterized by a five-fold coordinated Ti.

Keywords: nano-TiO₂; XAS; amorphisation
PACS: 61.05.cj, 64.70.Nd, 62.50.-p, 64.70.K-

INTRODUCTION

Titanium oxide can be found in a number of crystallographic phases, some of which are stabilized only under high pressure or recovered by decompression to atmospheric pressure. The increase in surface to bulk ratio when the grain size reaches the nano-scale generally induces new physical properties, including unusual pressure responses.

The behaviour under pressure of TiO₂ anatase is well known[1] and appears to be grain-size dependant: a transition to a baddeleyite structure is observed around 13 GPa, sometimes with or without an intermediate α–PbO₂ structure occurring. In very small grains (less than 10 nm), the starting anatase material is stable to higher pressure than in the bulk analog and pressure induced amorphisation (PIA) occurs at ~20 GPa [2,3].

The purpose of this study is to monitor the local environment of Ti well into the regime of PIA (~30 GPa) for the nanometric (6 nm) form of TiO₂ anatase, for comparison with the behavior of the bulk analog..

CP1092, *Synchrotron Radiation in Materials Science: 6ᵗʰ International Conference*, edited by R. Magalhaes-Paniago
© 2009 American Institute of Physics 978-0-7354-0625-4/09/$25.00

EXPERIMENTAL

Samples of nano-anatase TiO_2 with an average grain size of 6 nm were synthesized from $TiCl_4$ by the hydrothermal method, and characterization of the nano-anatase starting material was made by using both TEM and by X-ray diffraction. XAS (X-ray Absorption Spectroscopy) measurements have involved a special diamond anvil cell where the total thickness of the diamond along the beam has been reduced to 1 mm in order to allow transmission experiments. These experiments have been performed on the LUCIA beamline located at the Swiss Light Source.

The spectra of the reference samples (bulk anatase, and its high pressure derivatives) have been obtained in the same high pressure cell starting from micron grain size anatase. Several series of compression - decompression cycles have been done on new fillings of the cell of samples originating from the same batch.

All the data have been analyzed using the IFEFFIT package where the same parameters have been applied to the analysis of each of the spectra.

RESULTS

Fig. 1 shows the most relevant results of the behavior of nano anatase under pressure. As shown in Fig. 1(b), the pressure induced amorphization is evident in the 30 GPa measurement, where the second shell has completely disappeared in the Fourier Transform.

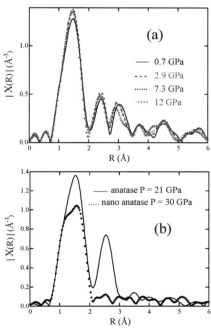

Figure 1 - Evolution of the Fourier Transform of the EXAFS oscillations of nano-TiO_2 showing , in panel (a), the evolution to a different structural phase above 12 GPa and in panel (b), the signatures of amorphization at 30 GPa.

But this pathway to amorphization seems to involve intermediate steps. Up to 12 - 15 GPa, the mid-range order around Ti atoms does not change much, and it can be, at each pressure step, decribed as a linear combination of the ambient pressure result and that of an intermediate phase onset at ~12 GPa. Above 15 and up to 30 GPa, the combination involves this intermediate phase and the final amorphous product. The nature of this intermediate phase depends on the starting experimental conditions. It is mostly characterized by a change of mid-range order, although this is difficult to model. In one series of experiments, this phase intermediate appearing at 12 - 15 GPa has been identified as the α-PbO_2 type also found in bulk anatase under pressure. This is clearly seen in Fig. 2 which compares the corresponding Fourier Transforms. The signature from α-PbO_2 comes from the second and third coordination shells, which differs appreciably from those in bulk anatase.

The first oxygen shell around the Ti atom can be ascribed to the new amorphous compound having 3±0.5 O at 1.89 Å and 3±0.5 O at 2.07 Å. The average Ti-O distance is larger than in the case of the octahedral environment of pure bulk anatase, therefore the amorphization is likely accompanied by an increase of the oxygen coordination, but this increase is within the error bars of an EXAFS determination of the coordination number.

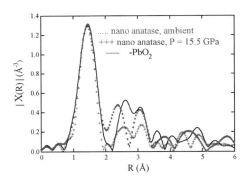

Figure 2 - Fourier Transforms of the data for bulk anatase, anatase transformed under pressure to the α-PbO_2 structure and nano-TiO_2 at 15.5 GPa in one series of experiments

Upon release to ambient pressure, a new phase is observed with Ti atoms mainly in five-fold coordination. The EXAFS analysis shows that the titanium atoms are now surrounded by 2±0.5 O at 1.84 Å and 2.5±0.5 O at 2.06 Å as evidenced by the amplitude of the first peak of the Fourier Transform (Fig. 3 (a)). This phase seems to present again some degree of mid-range order since a second shell is definitely present. A more precise description of this structure would not be reliable given the limitations of the EXAFS pressure data. Fig 3. (b) shows selected pre-edge spectra after removing the main rising edge component. The strong decrease of the pre-peaks at 4972 and 4974 eV at 30 GPa is in line with the amorphization process already described by the Fourier Transforms. Moreover, the strong peak obtained around 4971 eV when the pressure is fully released resembles that observed for nanocrystalline sol-gel anatase samples[4]. This has been interpreted as a signature of five-fold coordinated titanium, in agreement with the EXAFS result. This feature is also present in the nano-anatase spectrum at ambient pressure, in which low-coordinated surface atoms are to be anticipated.

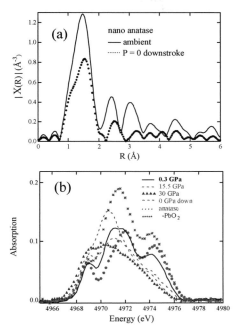

Figure 3 - a) The Fourier Transforms of pristine nano-anatase and the recovered product after a full compression - decompression cycle showing the decrease in oxygen coordination number around Ti atoms. b) Titanium pre-edge peaks of the nano-TiO_2 sample for several pressures.

CONCLUSIONS

EXAFS experiments under pressure reveal new information about the local structure around Ti atoms in nano-TiO_2 during the PIA process. In particular there is evidence of an intermediate phase appearing at 12 - 15 GPa prior to amorphisation. Furthermore the sample may follow different structural pathways prior to culminating in the high density amorphous end-product. Finally, a new phase, with mostly five-fold coordinated Ti, is identified after full decompression of this HDA phase to ambient conditions.

REFERENCES

1. T. Arlt, M. Bernejo, M.A. Blanco, L. Gerward, J.Z. Jiang, J. Staum Olsen and J.M. Recio, Phys. Rev. B **61**, 14414 (2000)
2. V. Swamy, A. Kuznetsov, L.S. Dubrovinsky, P.F. McMillan, V.B. Prakapenka, G. Shen and B.C. Muddle, Phys. Rev. Lett. 96, 135702 (2006)
3. G.R. Hearne, J. Zhao, A.M. Dawe, V. Pischedda, M. Maaza, M.K. Nieuwoudt, P. Kibasomba, O. Nemraoui and J.D. Comins, Phys. Rev. B **70**, 134102 (2004)
4. V.Luca, S. Djajanti and R.F. Howe, J.Phys.Chem. B 102, 10650 (1998)

In situ time-resolved X-ray diffraction studies of Fe$_2$O$_3$ and Cu,Cr-Fe$_2$O$_3$ catalysts for the water-gas shift reaction

Daniela Zanchet[a,*], Cristiane B. Rodella[a], Laura J.S. Lopes[a,b], Marco A. Logli[c], Valéria P. Vicentini[c], Wen Wen[b], Jonathan C. Hanson[b], José A. Rodriguez[b]

[a] *Brazilian Synchrotron Light Laboratory Sincrotron, CP 6192, 13083-971, Campinas SP, Brazil*
[b] *Chemistry Department, Federal University of Rio de Janeiro Rio de Janeiro, RJ,,Brazil*
[c] *Oxiteno S.A. Ind. & Com., Av. Ayrton S. da Silva 3001, 09380-440, Mauá SP, Brazil*
[d] *Chemistry Department, BrookhaVen National Laboratory, Upton, New York, 1197.,USA*
*Corresponding author: fax: (55) 19-3512-1004, e-mail: zanchet@lnls.br.

Abstract. The activation process and performance of Fe$_2$O$_3$ and an industrial Cu,Cr-Fe$_2$O$_3$ catalyst for the water-gas shift reaction were analysed by *in situ* time-resolved X-ray diffraction. We show that the catalytic activity in the case of Fe$_2$O$_3$ is related to the Fe$_2$O$_3$ → Fe$_3$O$_4$ transformation. However, in the case of the industrial Cu,Cr-Fe$_2$O$_3$ catalyst, the presence of Cu has a major effect, and strongly increases the catalytic activity, even before the full transformation to Fe$_3$O$_4$ takes place. The smaller Fe$_3$O$_4$ crystalline domains, detected by diffraction, should also contribute to make the industrial Cu,Cr-Fe$_2$O$_3$ the most active catalyst.

Keywords: Enter Keywords here.
PACS: Replace this text with PACS numbers; choose from this list:
http://www.aip.org/pacs/index.html

INTRODUCTION

The water gas shift (WGS) reaction, where carbon monoxide and steam are converted to carbon dioxide and hydrogen, is an important step in several industrial processes [1,2].

$$CO(g) + H_2O(g) \Leftrightarrow CO_2(g) + H_2(g) \tag{1}$$

In an industrial process, the reaction is carried out in two stages, known as HTS reaction (*High Temperature Shift*) and LTS reaction (*Low Temperature Shift*) and the catalysts used in each stage are optimized to operate at temperatures of about 450°C and and 200°C, respectively [1,2].
The most common industrial HTS catalyst is based on iron oxide particles with the addition of promoters, such as chromium and copper [2]. It is usually commercialized

CP1092, *Synchrotron Radiation in Materials Science: 6th International Conference,* edited by R. Magalhaes-Paniago
© 2009 American Institute of Physics 978-0-7354-0625-4/09/$25.00

as hematite (α-Fe$_2$O$_3$), that is converted *in situ* to magnetite (Fe$_3$O$_4$) during the activation process, which is the iron active phase in the HTS reaction. In this work, we address the activation and the performance in isothermal operation of an industrial HTS catalyst by *in situ* time-resolved X-ray diffraction (XRD). The evolution of the crystalline structure of the catalyst under WGS reaction conditions is followed by XRD, at the same time that its catalytic activity is measured. The HTS catalyst before activation is composed by hematite promoted with Cr and Cu (Cu,Cr-Fe$_2$O$_3$) and for comparison, a sample of pure hematite (Fe$_2$O$_3$) was also studied.

EXPERIMENTAL

The Cu,Cr-Fe$_2$O$_3$ catalyst was provided by Oxiteno S.A. Ind. & Com. (Mauá-SP, Brazil). The concentration is about 2% CuO, 8% Cr$_2$O$_3$ and 90% Fe$_2$O$_3$. A pure Fe$_2$O$_3$ catalyst was produced in a similar way. The results of specific surface area (S$_{BET}$) for the Fe$_2$O$_3$, and Cu,Cr-Fe$_2$O$_3$ catalysts were 72 and 59 m^2/g, respectively.

The major changes in the crystalline structure of the WGS catalysts and correlation with their catalytic activity were monitored by *in situ* time-resolved XRD. XRD patterns were obtained at the beam line X7B (λ=0.922 Å) of the National Synchrotron Light Source (NSLS) at Brookhaven National Laboratory [3-6]. Complementary data was obtained at the XRD2 beamline (λ=1.756 Å) at the Brazilian Synchrotron Light Source (LNLS). The WGS reaction was carried out isothermally at 350 and 430 ^{0}C, with a flow of 1% CO/He gas mixture through a water bubbler The relative ratio of water vapor pressure to CO in the feed gas mixture was around 1. A typical process took several hours, using a heating rate of 2°C/min. During the whole process, the WGS reaction was monitored by measuring the concentrations of the residual gases with a 0-200 amu quadrupole mass spectrometer while *in situ* diffraction patterns were collected.

RESULTS AND DISCUSSION

Figure 1 shows the XRD patterns of the Cu,Cr-Fe$_2$O$_3$ catalyst, where the typical lines of Fe$_2$O$_3$ and minor peaks of metallic Fe and Fe$_3$O$_4$ can be identified. The weak diffraction peaks of Fe did not disappear when the catalysts was calcined in O$_2$ at elevated temperatures. This suggests that the pure Fe is located in the core of the Cu,Cr-Fe$_2$O$_3$ particles and one can expect that it will have only a minor effect on the WGS activity of the system. No extra diffraction lines of Cu or Cr oxides could be detected, suggesting that the Cu and Cr are embedded in the lattice of Fe$_2$O$_3$. In the case of the Fe$_2$O$_3$catalyst, at the beginning, the sample presents the typical diffraction pattern of hematite.

The in situ XRD analysis showed different behavior of the two samples; while the Fe$_2$O$_3$ $\rightarrow$ Fe$_3$O$_4$ transformation takes place below 350°C in the Fe$_2$O$_3$ sample, it could be barely detected at this temperature in the Cu,Cr-Fe$_2$O$_3$ catalyst. In this case, during the isothermal conditions at 350°C the Fe$_2$O$_3$ $\rightarrow$ Fe$_3$O$_4$ transformation progresses slowly, and the full transformation is only achieved when the temperature increased to 430°C. The presence of Cu and Cr inside the lattice of iron oxide clearly retards the $Fe_2O_3 \rightarrow Fe_3O_4$ transformation, but surprisingly, the $Cu,Cr-Fe_2O_3$ system is already a very good catalyst for the WGS reaction at temperatures as low as 200°C, as can be seen in Figure 1. Cu sites probably compensate for the lack of an active Fe_3O_4 phase. For a $Cu,Cr-Fe_2O_3$ system, a complete $Fe_2O_3 \rightarrow Fe_3O_4$ transformation takes place after increasing the temperature to 430 °C, and from this point the XRD pattern stops changing.

Comparing the production of H_2 on the two catalysts and after normalization by the mass and taking into account the initial differences in surface area, we can conclude that the industrial $Cu,Cr-Fe_2O_3$ catalyst presents much higher performance for the WGS reaction in the analysed conditions. Although the sites present in Fe_3O_4 do have catalytic activity, they cannot match the activity associated with the Cu sites. Peak-width analysis of the Fe_3O_4 diffraction patterns in the two samples indicate that the particle size of the $Cu,Cr-Fe_2O_3$ catalyst formed during the activation is substantially smaller than the particle sizes of the Fe_3O_4 of the Fe_2O_3 catalyst. This also should help to make $Cu,Cr-Fe_2O_3$ the most active catalyst.

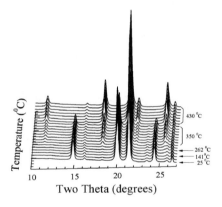

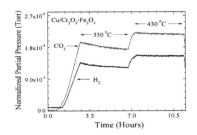

Figure 1 – Above: *In situ* XRD patterns collected during the WGS on $Cu,Cr-Fe_2O_3$ catalyst at 350 °C and 430 °C; Below: Corresponding catalytic activity.

CONCLUSIONS

In situ time-resolved X-ray diffraction performed during WGS reaction in three iron oxide based catalysts revealed new and interesting features related to their activation process and performace. For the Fe_2O_3 and Cr-Fe_2O_3 catalysts, the catalytic activities are related to the $Fe_2O_3 \rightarrow Fe_3O_4$ transformation. The present of Cr embedded in the Fe_2O_3 lattice shifts the phase transition temperature to higher value and it is probably related to the fact the Cr_2O_3 and Fe_2O_3 have the same crystallographic structure. In the case of the industrial Cu,Cr-Fe_2O_3 catalyst, the presence of Cu has a major effect, and strongly increases the catalytic activity. Surprisingly, a good catalytic activity is already detected at low temperatures, when the $Fe_2O_3 \rightarrow Fe_3O_4$ transformation has barely started. Its smaller Fe_3O_4 crystalline domains should also contribute to high activity of the Cu,Cr-Fe_2O_3 catalyst.

ACKNOWLEDGMENTS

This work was supported by the Brazilian Synchrotron Light Laboratory (LNLS) and CNPq (Brazil), and by the U.S. Department of Energy (DOE), Office of Basic Energy Sciences, Chemical Science Division (DE-AC02-98CH10886). The NSLS is supported by the Materials and Chemical Sciences Divisions of DOE. The samples were provided by Oxiteno S.A. Ind. & Com. (Brazil).

REFERENCES

1. L. Lloyd, D.E. Ridler, M.V. Twigg in *Catalysis Handbook*, Martyn V. Twigg, Ed.; Manson Publishing, Englang, 1996, p. 283.
2. K. Knözinger in *Handbook of Heterogeneous Catalysis*, G. Ertl, H. Knözinger, J. Weitkamp, Eds., vol. 4, 1997, p. 1831.
3. X. Wang, J.A. Rodriguez, J. C. Hanson, M. Perez, and J. Evans, *J. Chem. Phys.*, 2005, *123*, 221101.
4. P.J. Chupas, M.F. Ciraolo, J.C. Hanson, and C. Grey, *J. Am. Chem. Soc.,*2001, *123*, 1694.
5. W. Wen. J. Liu, M.G. White, N. Marinkovic, J.C. Hanson, and J.A. Rodriguez, *Catal. Lett.* 2007, *113*, 1.
6. X. Wang, J.A. Rodriguez, J.C. Hanson, D. Gamarra, A. Martínez-Arias, and M. Fernández-García, *J. Phys. Chem. B*, 2006, *110* , 428.

Investigation of Stress Relaxation in Filled Elastomers by XPCS with Heterodyne Detection

Françoise Ehrburger-Dolle[a], Isabelle Morfin[a], Françoise Bley[b],
Frédéric Livet[b], Gert Heinrich[c], Sven Richter[c], Luc Piché[d], Mark Sutton[d]

[a]*Laboratoire de Spectrométrie Physique, UMR5588 CNRS-UJF, 38402 Saint-Martin d'Hères, France*
[b]*SIMAP, UMR5266 CNRS-UJF-INPG, 38402 Saint-Martin d'Hères, France*
[c]*Leibniz Institute of Polymer Research, IPF, 01069 Dresden, Germany*
[d]*Physics Department, McGill University, Montréal, Québec, Canada H3A 2T8*

Abstract. XPCS with heterodyne detection (HD-XPCS) is a new original method that gives information about the dynamics of filler aggregates during stress relaxation and its relation to the macroscopic mechanical behavior measured *in situ*.

Keywords: X-ray photon correlation spectroscopy, heterodyne detection, filled elastomers
PACS: 78.70.Ck; 81.05.Qk; 83.80.Wx

INTRODUCTION

Despite a very large amount of work performed since more than 50 years, the nonlinearity in viscoelastic properties of filled rubbers is still poorly understood. Various explanations have been proposed as filler deagglomeration under strain and reagglomeration during recovery[1]. To investigate this assumption, we performed, a few years ago, SAXS[2] and XPCS[3] with homodyne and heterodyne (HD) detection. For the latter, the samples investigated (cross-linked and uncross-linked carbon black filled Ethylene-Propylene Rubber (EPR)) were stretched at 100% elongation and XPCS measurements were performed during recovery at zero strain. This first series of XPCS measurements yielded the following conclusions: i) the velocity of the filler particles is larger in the uncross-linked sample than in the cross-linked one and decreases with aging; ii) the relaxation time scales as q^{-1} and, iii) the correlation functions are compressed exponentials with an exponent μ ranging between 1.5 and 2. These features suggest occurrence of *jamming*.

In order to go one step further in the investigation of the local stress relaxation in filled elastomers, we recently investigated an extended series of elastomers filled with silica Aerosil or carbon black with *in situ* stress-strain data monitoring. The goal of this communication is to show what kind of information can be obtained by combining heterodyne and homodyne XPCS with stress-strain measurements performed on cross-linked samples.

CP1092, *Synchrotron Radiation in Materials Science: 6th International Conference*, edited by R. Magalhaes-Paniago
© 2009 American Institute of Physics 978-0-7354-0625-4/09/$25.00

EXPERIMENTAL

XPCS measurements were performed on the XOR beamline 8-ID (APS) in similar experimental conditions as for the previous series[3]. The major difference was the use of a small stretching machine that elongates the sample symmetrically and measures the force. Samples consisted of an elastomer (Ethylene Propylene Diene Monomer, EPDM, rubber) filled with carbon black N330 (CB), hydoxylated pyrogenic silica (A200) or hydrophobic Aerosil 200 (R974). The volume fraction of filler was 0.1 or 0.2 and cross-linking was performed by means of dicumyl peroxide. The present communication focuses on two samples of cross-linked filled EPDM: the first one filled with A200 and the second one filled with carbon black (CB). For both samples, the volume fraction of filler is close to 0.2. As for all investigated samples, the elongation was increased stepwise to 20, 40, 60% then decreased to 40, 20, 0% and increased again (second stretch) up to the same values as in the first stretching series. During each step (nearly 4200s), two homodyne and two heterodyne measurements were alternately performed while the relaxation of the force, at constant length, was recorded. The direction of the stretch was vertical. The area detector covered approximately one quadrant (azimuthal angles from $\varphi=165°$ to $300°$). Multi-speckle analysis was achieved by means of the software *coherent* (Matthew A. Borthwick and Peter Falus, 22 november 2003 © MIT 1996) available on the beamline. Ensemble averaging was made in all $\delta\varphi$-δq domains of the area detector with $\delta\varphi=5.6°$ and $\delta q=1.02\times10^{-3}$ Å^{-1}.

RESULTS AND DISCUSSION

A200 and CB filled EPDM at zero strain after a first cycle of elongation (previous maximum equal to 60%)

Owing to the relative velocity between the sample and the static reference (compacted Aerosil 200), the correlation function acquires a phase factor of $\exp(i\vec{q}.\vec{v}t)$. We can define $\omega = \vec{q}.\vec{v} = qv\cos(\varphi-\varphi_0)$. Figure 1 shows an example of heterodyne correlation functions along two perpendicular directions.

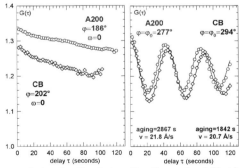

FIGURE 1. Heterodyne correlation function in two directions φ ($q=6.78\times10^{-3}$ Å^{-1}) for A200 and CB filled EPDM at 0% elongation after the first cycle of elongation ($\varphi_{stretch}=270°$).

The experimental data are fitted with Eq.1[3].

$$g_{2het}(q,\varphi,t) = 1 + A + B\exp[-2(\tau/\tau_0)^\mu] + C\cos\omega\tau\exp[-(\tau/\tau_0)^\mu] \tag{1}$$

with : $A = \beta(1-x)^2$, $B = \beta x^2$, $C = 2\beta x(1-x)$ (2)

x is the mixing coefficient x ($x = I_s(q)/[I_s(q) + I_r(q)]$). The value of φ_0 is obtained by plotting $G(\tau)$ for all angles φ, at a given q, and finding φ at which the oscillation frequency ω is maximum. Despite the fact that the mixing coefficient x could be determined from the static scattering curves for sample $I_s(q)$ and reference $I_r(q)$, it is handled as a free parameter for the fit; consistency between the two x values is checked. The systems investigated are out of equilibrium; one of the goals is to investigate the evolution of the dynamical characteristics during aging (t_a) under constant (or zero) strain. To this end, correlation functions were determined over the shortest realistic delay times. It follows that, in HD conditions, the values of τ_0 and μ (not reported) may not be relevant. Homodyne data are fitted with Eq. 3

$$g_{2hom}(q,\varphi,\tau) = 1 + \beta\exp[-2(\tau/\tau_0)^\mu] \tag{3}$$

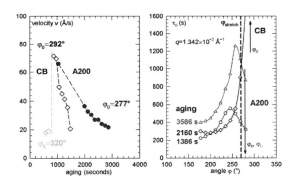

FIGURE 2. (*left*) Evolution of the velocity v during aging of the carbon black (CB) and silica (A200) filled EPDM at zero elongation (strain back to zero) obtained by HD detection; (*right*) angular dependence of the homodyne relaxation time (from Eq. 3).

Fig.1 (*right*) and Fig.2, lead the following information:
- for A200 and CB, velocities reach similar values but the direction of $\vec{v}$ is different (for A200, $\vec{v}$ is nearly parallel to stretch).
- during aging, v decreases faster for CB than for A200 sample (Fig.2, *left*); for CB, the direction of $\vec{v}$ changes with aging time.
- for CB and A200, τ_0 (homodyne) is minimum for $\omega=0$ (in fact, Eq.3 may not be strictly valid when $\omega \neq 0$); the exponent μ (Eq.3) is always close to 2; in all cases, τ_0 (for $\omega=0$) scales as q^{-1}.

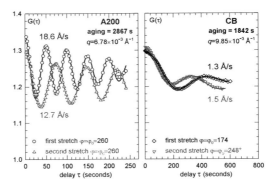

FIGURE 3. Comparison of heterodyne correlations for A200 (*left*) and CB (*right*) samples under strain (60% elongation) during first and second cycle of strain.

Fig.3 shows that the HD $G(\tau)$ curves for A200 and CB samples under strain, are very different:
- for A200, fit with Eq. 1 indicates that v is smaller during the second stretch at same aging time.
- for CB, v is much smaller than for A200; fit with Eq. 1 requires to multiply B (Eq. 2) by an empirical factor F that increases with q; the physical meaning of this feature is still not clear; interestingly, $\bar{v}$ is still nearly perpendicular to the stretching direction at $t_a=1840$ s during the first stretch.

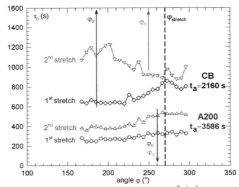

FIGURE 4. Homodyne detection: variation of τ_0 ($q=1.34\times10^{-2}$ Å^{-1}) with φ at two different aging times. μ fluctuates between 1.9 and 2.

The variation of τ_0 determined in homodyne conditions (Fig.4) is also very different for A200 and CB:
- for A200, at the same t_a, τ_0 (along direction φ where $\omega=0$) is larger in the second stretch than in the first one and similar to that obtained for A200 at zero strain (Fig.2, *right*), at the same t_a.

- for CB, τ_0 is smaller along direction φ where $\omega=0$ than along direction φ_0; τ_0 is large as compared to its value measured at zero strain (Fig.2, *right*)

CONCLUSIONS

Analysis of all data obtained by XPCS as well as the stress-strain curves is not achieved yet, which precludes an extensive interpretation of the observations reported here. It may be suggested, as working clues, that CB which strongly interacts with the elastomer matrix after cross-linking, behaves as a jammed system (or a glass) under strain, while A200 (weak interaction) behaves as a gel. This work points out that heterodyne XPCS brings very new insights in the field of stress relaxation in filled elastomers.

REFERENCES

1. G. Heinrich, M. Klüppel, *Adv. Polym. Sci.* 2002, *160*, 1.
2. F. Ehrburger-Dolle; F. Bley; E. Geissler; F. Livet; I. Morfin; C. Rochas *Macromol. Symposia* 2003, *200*, 157.
3. F. Livet; F. Bley; F. Ehrburger-Dolle; I. Morfin; E. Geissler; M. Sutton *J. Sync. Rad.* 2006, *13*, 453.

ACKNOWLEDGMENTS

Use of the APS was supported by the DOE, Office of Basic Energy Sciences, under Contract No. W-31-109-Eng-38. The authors thank René Jurk (IPF Dresden) for the preparation of filled EPDM samples.

Electronic structure of d^0 vanadates obtained by x-ray absorption and emission spectroscopies.

G. Herrera[1*], J. Jimenez-Mier[2], E. Chavira[3], A. Moewes[4], R. Wilks[4]

[1]Posgrado en Ciencias Químicas, Universidad Nacional Autónoma de México, 70-360,04510 México D. F., MEXICO.
[2]Instituto de Ciencias Nucleares, Universidad Nacional Autónoma de México, 70-360, 04510 México D. F., MEXICO.
[3]Instituto de Investigaciones en Materiales, Universidad Nacional Autónoma de México, 70-360, 04510 México D. F., MEXICO.
[4]University of Saskatchewan, Departament of Physics, 116 Science Place, Saskatoon, SK S7N 5E2, Canada.
*guillermo.herrera@nucleares.unam.mx

Abstract. We present experimental results for x-ray absorption at the $L_{2,3}$-edge of vanadium in V_2O_5, YVO_4 and $LaVO_4$ compounds and at the $M_{4,5}$-edge of lanthanum in $LaVO_4$ compound. The data are interpreted in terms of the multiplet structure of the transition metal ion V^{5+} (d^0) and rare earth ion La^{3+} (d^{10}). The data are compared with calculations in the free-ion approximation for La and including the effects of the D_{4h} ligand field and charge transfer for V. These calculations allow a direct interpretation of the absorption spectra. Good overall agreement between experiment and theory is found. We also show resonant x-ray emission (XES) data for these compounds obtained at the top of the L_2 excitation.

INTRODUCTION

X-Ray absorption spectroscopy (XAS) in the vicinity of the $L_{2,3}$ edge of the transition metal and the $M_{4,5}$ edge of the rare earth gives information about the unoccupied states of $3d$ and $4f$ symmetry that can be reached by electromagnetic excitation of $2p_{1/2, \, 3/2}$ or $3d_{3/2, \, 5/2}$ core electrons [1]. The $2p$ hole in V is filled by x-ray emission (XES), which result in decay into the ground state of the system (elastic emission) or into excited states of the ground configuration (inelastic emission). XES thus provides information about the excited states of the ground configuration of the transition metal ion. The interpretation of XAS of the transition metal compounds is aided by ligand-field charge-transfer calculations [2].

The experiment took place at the soft x-ray end station of beamline 8.0.1 of the Advanced Light Source of Lawrence Berkeley National Laboratory. The V_2O_5 was

CP1092, *Synchrotron Radiation in Materials Science: 6th International Conference*, edited by R. Magalhaes-Paniago
© 2009 American Institute of Physics 978-0-7354-0625-4/09/$25.00

commercial powders (CERAC, 99.9 %). YVO_4 and $LaVO_4$ were prepared by solid state reaction (SSR) and sol-gel acrylamide polymerization [3].

RESULTS AND DISCUSSION

In Fig. 1 we present an example of a comparison between absorption spectrum (total electron yield, TEY) of YVO_4 prepared by SSR and the results obtained by a calculation that includes a D_{4h} ligand field and charge transfer effects. The agreement between theory and experiment is also very good for all the other compounds.
In the calculation the ground state of the system is considered to be an admixture of a d^0 and d^1 $\underline{L}$ states, ($\underline{L}$ represents a hole in the ligand). The observed weights of the d^0 and d^1 $\underline{L}$ configurations are 50% and 50% for V_2O_5 compared to 75% and 25% for the vanadates.

In Fig. 1 we also show an emission spectrum for YVO_4 (SSR) excited at (a). One observes a rather small feature due to elastic emission, an inelastic peak with a 7.4 eV energy loss and a broad peak that corresponds to normal decay into a non-resonantly produced $2p_{3/2}$ hole. The energy loss found in the less ionic compound V_2O_5 is 6.7 eV. These values are in good agreement with the calculation. Therefore the inelastic peak corresponds to transition into a charge transfer state in the ground configuration.

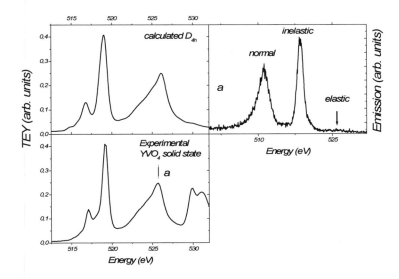

Fig 1. Comparison between experiment and theory for YVO_4 prepared by SSR. Bottom left, TEY spectrum; Top left, charge transfer calculated absorption. Top right: emission spectrum for an excitation energy of 527 eV (a).

REFERENCES

1. A. Kotani *Eur. Phys. J. B* 2005 **47**, 3.
2. F. M. F. de Groot *Coordination Chemistry Reviews* 2005 **249**, 31.
3. G. Herrera E. Chavira, J. Jiménez-Mier, L. Baños, J. Guzmán, C. Flores, *J. Sol-Gel Sci. Technol.* 2008 in press.

A Versatile Hemispherical Great Area X-ray Detector for Synchrotron Radiation

Rodolfo Figueroa and Felipe Belmar

Laboratorio XRF, Departmento de Ciencias Físicas
Universidad de La Frontera, Temuco, Chile, figueror@ufro.cl

This work presents an X-ray detector with fullerene C60 semi spherical geometry constituted by a set of small cylindrical proportional counter units with needles anodes, which are located in the surface of an hemispherical plastic support. The sample to be analyzed is placed on the center of the hemisphere base. The radiation may enter by one of its flanks or through the hemisphere top. The hemispherical zone that exists between the holder sample base and the proportional counters can be vacuumed, aired or filled with counter gas.

Keywords: Ray Detector
PACS: 07.85.Fv

The great intensity of synchrotron light beams and their increase brings with it the need for faster and faster detectors able to respond efficiently with high count rates and maintain a certain degree of energy resolution without becoming saturated, thereby avoiding the need for large beam attenuations when an effective response is required. Gas proportional counters present certain characteristics [1-6], making them ideal candidates for these requirements and can already reach count rates in x-ray detection with an energy resolution in the region of 20% of the energy of 5.9 eV. If the count rate must be increased, proportional counters with needle anodes present an interesting alternative due to their great geometric versatility and the integration that can be achieved with them. Their adequate integration makes it possible to secure high count rates, which makes them a sound alternative in applications with synchrotron light or intense X-ray tubes. In dedicated XRF applications where a large energy resolution is not required, an attempt is made to determine one or more specific elements at trace level, allowing applications in which the saturation that normally happens with conventional solid state detectors is minimized or avoided. These units could be a good, low-cost alternative capable of improving current detection limits.

Several authors have worked on developing proportional detectors with point or needle anodes [7-10]; however, until now they have not been sufficiently developed, with their first applications being devoted to a sensitive position. Unlike a wire anode, a point anode allows for directly localized detection, greater robustness and geometric versatility. Electrically, they behave in a manner very similar to that of a proportional counter with a wire anode, with a spherical electric field around a point in contrast to a cylindrical field of wire anodes with a multiplication zone with practically homogenous gain around a hemispheric needle point.

CP1092, *Synchrotron Radiation in Materials Science: 6th International Conference*, edited by R. Magalhaes-Paniago
© 2009 American Institute of Physics 978-0-7354-0625-4/09/$25.00

It is important that the points be properly hemispheric and of very similar diameters when working with several in parallel so as not to affect the energy resolution of the set. This requirement involves a careful selection of the needle points.

This study presents a hemispheric detector based on a set of small cylindrical proportional detectors with needle anodes and a front window, able to measure practically all the fluorescent radiation generated in the sample that is collected in its interior.

DESCRIPTION

Every proportional counter is in the shape of a small aluminum cylinder with a front window (Fig.1c), with a central anode formed by a selected steel sewing needle (Fig. 1d). The shape of the point and the diameter of the needles were selected using a digital microscope and a projector-type data show. Each one is micro hemispheric of approximately 80μm. The general detector is made up of a set of 15 proportional counters as described, able to detect practically all the radiation emitted from the sample, which is in the center of the sphere that forms the hemisphere at a solid angle of 2π. Ten of the counters are located at the positions corresponding to hexagons and the other five in the positions of pentagons, with diameters of 12.5 and 10.0 cm, respectively. Each proportional counter is approximately the same distance from the sample. The diameter of these counters bears relation to the diameters corresponding to the circumferences inscribed between hexagons and pentagons. This configuration makes it possible to greatly improve the geometrical detection efficiency. Every proportional counter can work independently or in parallel, in the latter it can integrate the count of all the units, which involves a considerable increase in the count rate by one factor near the number of proportional counters.

FIGURE 1. General view of the hemispheric detector (a), Open detector showing (b), base carrying sample, lid and the proportional counters (c) with needle anodes (d).

RESULTS AND DISCUSSION

Figure 2, the pulse amplitude characteristic of each counter based on the voltage applied is presented; note that these respond with a proportional range that is between 1350 and 1600 V. In Figure 3 is the count rate based on the voltage applied; in this case, the plateau zone of the previous pulse amplitude and the area of limited proportionality, i.e., from 1150 v to the beginning of the Geiger zone, 1800 V. For the energy resolution of the counters, a ^{55}Fe source was used, with which a FWMH equal to 18% was determined for the Mn ka line of 5.9keV. This value turned out to be slightly lower than the resolution that has been obtained with similar proportional counters.

This is the in addition, the detection efficiency of these units was ascertained from the activity of the source and the incidental x-radiation intensity, considering all the processes of loss and attenuation in the different media and was compared with the effectively measured intensity for different energies using different mono elemental secondary targets. The experimental points were compared again with the calculated efficiency curve, considering the length from the window and to the anode (drift zone). This turned out to be close to 80% for the energy between 5 and 10 keV.

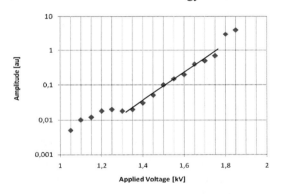

FIGURE 2. Pulse amplitude characteristic of each counter based on the voltage applied

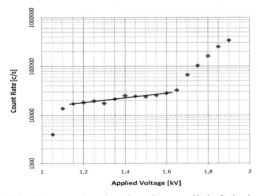

FIGURE 3. Count rate based on the voltage applied of a basic unit

CONCLUSIONS

It has been demonstrated that the base units base of the hemispheric detector presented behave like a proportional counter, the energy resolution of which is close to 18% for X-rays of 5.9 keV, independent of the angular position of the source.

The proportional operation zone was in a range between 1350 and 1650 V.

The integration of all the units plus the use of a gas count that allows for a greater electron migration velocity and the adaptation of suitable electronics will make high count rates possible.

The detection efficiency shown by each one of the count units is between 100% and 80% for the incident energy range from 2 to 15 keV, respectively, with gas atmospheric pressure.

The detector is low-cost, compact and highly versatile and will allow various applications related to soft x-ray detection.

ACKNOWLEDGMENTS

This study was supported by the Dirección de Investigación of the Universidad de La Frontera through Project EP 120515.

REFERENCES

1. M. P. Brown and K. A. Alkaa, K. Mitev and P. Ségur "A fast technique for Monte Carlo simulation of the process of gas multiplication in cylindrical proportional counters" *Nuclear Instruments and Methods in Physics Research Section A: 580, Issue 1, 21 September 2007, Pages 161-164*
2. M. Deptuch and T.Z. Kowalski "Performance of Ar/CO_2 filled proportional counters under high gas gain at high working gas pressure"*Nuclear Instruments and Methods in Physics Research Section A:*2007 , **572**, 1-1 ,181-183
3. J. E. Bateman "A general parametric model for the gain of gas avalanche counters with particular attention to non-cylindrical geometries" *Physics Reports*, 2003, **375**, 6, Pages 411-443.
4. K. Mitev, P. Ségur, A. Alkaa, M.C. Bordage, C. Furstoss, C. Khamphan, L. de Nardo, V. Conte and P. Colautti Study of non-equilibrium electron avalanches, application to proportional counters *Nuclear Instruments and Methods in Physics Research Section A:*, 2005, **538**, 1-3, 11, 672-685.
5. H. Date, K. Kondo, M. Shimozuma and H. Tagashira "Electron kinetics in proportional counters" *Nuclear Instruments and Methods in Physics Research Section A:* 2000 **451**, 3, 588-595.
6. Albul I and Isaev B. M., Choosing the operating point on the count rate characteristic of a cylindrical proportional counter, *Measurement Techniques*, 1968,11,12, 1686-1688.
7. Comby, G.; Mangeot. P. "Multi Needle Counter with Cathode Focusing" *Nuclear Science, IEEE Transactions,* 1980, 27, 1, 106 – 110.
8. Batemam J.E., "The pin detector- A simple, robust, cheap and effective nuclear radiation detector", *Nuclear Instrument and Method.* 1985, A238, 524-532.
9. Bateman J.E. "The imaging pin detector A smple and effective new imaging device for soft X-rays and soft beta emissions" *Nuclear Instrument and Method.* 1985, 240,1, 177-187.
10. Ranzetta GVT, Scott VD "Point anode proportional counters for the detection of soft X rays in microanalysis "*Journal Science. Instrument 1967.* 44 983-987.

Towards a better understanding of the structure of nano-minerals at ambient and extreme conditions.

John B. Parise[1,*], Lars Ehm[1], F. Marc Michel[1], Sytle Antao[2], Peter J. Chupas[2], Peter L. Lee[2], C. David Martin[2] and Sarvjit Shastri[2]

1. Stony Brook University, Department of Geosciences and Mineral Physics Institute
John.Parise@sunysb.edu, Lars.Ehm@sunysb.edu, Fredrick.Michel@sunysb.edu,
2. X-ray Science Division, Argonne National Laboratory, Argonne IL 60439, USA
santao@anl.gov, chupas@anl.gov, pllee@aps.anl.gov, Cmartin@anl.gov, SShastri@anl.gov

Abstract. The high-pressure (HP) behavior of nano-crystalline mackinawite (n-FeS) with particle sizes of 6, 7, and 8 nm has been investigated by high-energy X-ray total scattering and pair distribution function analysis. An irreversible first-order structural phase transition from tetragonal mackinawite to orthorhombic FeS-II was observed at about 3 GPa. The transition is induced by the closure of the van-der-Waals gap in the layered mackinawite structure. A grain size effect on the transition pressure and the compressibility was observed. The n-FeS study is an example of a broad class of nano-crystalline minerals where the total scattering (TS) approach provides significant new information on local-, intermediate- and long-range structure. Under extreme conditions, of pressure in this case, straightforward modifications allow quantitative descriptions of the transformations mechanisms.

Keywords: Materials Science, Synchrotron Radiation.
PACS: 81.00.00

INTRODUCTION

Defining the arrangement of atoms in nano-structured materials, and in particular nano-minerals, is challenging. The diffraction data obtained from these materials, compared to that available from the equivalent bulk material, is much degraded. Bragg peaks broaden and the build up of diffuse scattering, often ignored as increased background in Rietveld structure refinement, is significant as particle sizes approach the coherence length of the radiation used to study these materials. These changes in diffraction patterns impede efforts to interpret changes in the properties of nano-minerals under a variety of environmental conditions [1, 2], including those at HP [3, 4]. Further complicating structure determination at high-pressure is the use of capping agents to stabilize nano-materials from agglomerating or oxidizing. Data collected *in situ* often consist of a few broadened peaks and the information loss implied by this makes use of traditional crystallographic techniques, quite appropriate from bulk periodic materials, wholly inappropriate for the study of many geo-nano-materials.

Nano-crystalline iron sulfide (FeS) can be produced and stabilized without capping agents, in a variety of size distributions, and presents an opportunity to compare structure-property relationships directly with those of the bulk equivalent, and as a function of particle size. Further, by applying recently developed methodologies dependent on collection and analysis of high energy X-ray total scattering (Bragg + diffuse) data [5-8], *in situ* from samples in high pressure devices, we can draw conclusions based on structure models refined using these data.

Iron sulfides are of major importance in geological, environmental and planetary science [2]. The phase relations in this system are complex and not fully resolved. Recently, Michel *et al.* [2] showed that synthetic nano-crystalline FeS (n-FeS), similar to that formed in marine sediments from reaction of iron and hydrogen sulfide produced by sulfate-reducing microorganisms adopts the mackinawite structure.

The determination of the atomic structure of n-FeS is now possible due to the increasing availability of intense, focused, high-energy synchrotron radiation. These new experimental facilities allow the collection of X-ray total scattering data in pressure cells with good statistics at high reciprocal space values (i.e. 15-20 Å^{-1}). The pair distribution function (PDF) is obtained by Fourier transformation of the total elastic scattering data, which include the Bragg and the diffuse scattering contributions, and contains information of the short-, intermediate, and long-range distribution of interatomic distances. The resolution, sensitivity, and extended range of information obtained by this technique are essential for testing structural models of nano-crystalline materials.

Mackinawite (FeS) crystallizes in the space group *P*4/*nmm*, a=3.6735(4) Å and c=5.0328(7) Å. Iron occupies the Wyckoff position 2a (0,0,0) and sulfur the position 2b (0,0.5,0.25). The structure is composed of layers of edge-sharing FeS_4 tetrahedra stacked onto each other parallel to the c axis. The bonding in the layers is dominantly covalent whereas the layers are connected by van-der-Waals forces.

RESULTS AND DISCUSSION

High-energy TS data were collected from ambient pressure up to 9.2(2) GPa for n-FeS with particle sizes of 6, 7, and 8 nm. The evolution of the integrated diffraction patterns with pressure for the three particle sizes are shown in Figure 1. The disappearance of the 001 reflection of n-FeS at Q~1.2 Å^{-1} can be observed for all samples, indicating a pressure induced phase transition. The transition pressure is particle size dependent ranging from 3.0 for the larger particles to 3.7(2) GPa.

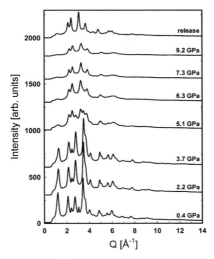

Figure 1 - Pressure dependence of the diffraction patterns of n-FeS with grain sizes of 6 nm (λ=0.124 Å). Disappearance of the 001 reflection (at $Q \sim 1$ Å^{-1}), is clearly visible above 3.7 GPa.

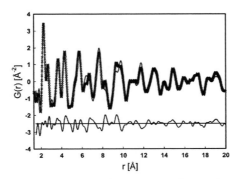

Figure 2 - Observed (crosses) and calculated (solid line) PDF of n-FeS-6 nm and a mackinawite model, respectively, at 0.4(2) GPa. The difference measured and calculated PDF is plotted at the bottom.

Figure 2 shows the pair distribution function (PDF) of the n-FeS-6 nm sample at 0.4(2) GPa and the fit of the mackinawite structure model to the data. The structure determination for the HP phase of mackinawite from the total scattering data is not straight forward, since nano-crystalline materials show diffraction patterns with very few and overlapping Bragg peaks, and a pronounced diffuse component making conventional crystallographic structure solution approaches inapplicable. However, the maxima in the PDF can be assigned to specific atomic pairs and allows developing an initial structural model for the high-pressure phase.

Three structures, Troilite and its high pressure polymorphs FeS-II and FeS-III [9], meet the distance and connectivity requirements derived from the PDF of the high-pressure phase. Fitting of the PDF to models for this structure suggests the MnP-type structure (FeS-II), an orthorhombically distorted variant of the NiAs structure type, is the HP phase of n-FeS.

CONCLUSION

The phase transition from n-FeS to FeS-II is observed from about 3 GPa. The TS/PDF approach described here and elsewhere offers great promise in deriving rigorously testable structure models for nano-materials, even at high pressures. Recent successes include new insights into the atomic arrangements in geo-nano-materials that have eluded characterization for decades [1]. However, nano-crystalline FeS adds a cautionary note to this promise by reminding us that the application of periodic structure models to the nano-world provides an approximation of the atomic arrangement, and that when closely related structure models need to be distinguished the data need to be of the highest quality and resolution.

ACKNOWLEDGMENTS

This work was supported by the following grants and contracts: U.S. DOE Contract DE-AC02-06CH11357 (APS) NSF-EAR-0217473, DE-FG02-94ER14466 and the State of Illinois (GeoSoilEnviroCARS), NSF-DMR-0452444, EAR-0510501, and CHE-0221934 (JBP)

REFERENCES

1. Michel, F. M., Ehm, L., Antao, S. M., Lee, P., Chupas, P. J., Liu, G., Strongin, D. R., Schoonen, M. A. A., Phillips, B. L. & Parise, J. B. *Science* 2007, *316*, 1726.
2. Michel, F. M., Antao, S. M., Chupas, P. J., Lee, P. L., Parise, J. B. & Schoonen, M. A. A. *Chem. Materials* 2005, *17*, 6246.
3. Ehm, L., Antao, S. M., Chen, J., Locke, D. R., Michel, M. F., Martin, C. D., Yu, T., Parise, J. B., Chupas, P. J., Lee, P. L., Shastri, S. D. & Guo, Q. *Powder Diff.* 2007, *22*, 180.
4. Parise, J. B., Antao, S. M., Michel, F. M., Martin, C. D., Chupas, P. J., Shastri, S. D. & Lee, P. L. *J. Synch. Rad.* 2005, *12*, 554.
5. Billinge, S. J. L. *Z. Kristall.* 2004, *219*, 117.
6. Billinge, S. J. L. & Kanatzidis, M. G. *Chem. Commun.* 2004, 749.
7. Billinge, S. J. L. & Levin, I. *Science* 2007, *316*, 561.
8. Chupas, P. J., Qiu, X., Hanson, J. C., Lee, P. L., Grey, C. P. & Billinge, S. L. *J. Appl. Cryst.* 2004, *36*, 1342.
9. Marshall, W. G., Loveday, J. S., Nelmes, R. J., Klotz, S., Hamel, G., Besson, J. M. & Parise, J. B. *Rev. High Press. Sci. Technol.* 1998, *7*, 565.

SAXS Analysis of Embedded Pt Nanocrystals Irradiated with Swift Heavy Ions

R. Giulian[*1], P. Kluth[1], D.J. Sprouster[1], L.L. Araujo[1], A.P. Byrne[1], D.J. Cookson[2] and M.C. Ridgway[1]

[1]Research School of Physical Sciences and Engineering, Australian National University, Australia.
[2] Australian Synchrotron Research Program, Argone, IL, USA

Abstract. Elongated Pt nanocrystals (NCs) formed in SiO_2 by ion implantation, thermal annealing and swift heavy ion irradiation were analyzed by small-angle X-ray scattering (SAXS) and transmission electron microscopy (TEM) measurements. Transmission SAXS measurements were performed in samples aligned at different angles relative to the photon beam resulting in non-isotropic scattering and thus enabling the three dimensional analysis of the NCs. Selected angular sectors of the detector were integrated and analyzed separately, leading to the individual evaluation of both the major and minor dimensions of the rod-shaped NCs. This method enables the use of well established spherical models for the SAXS data analysis and yielded excellent agreement with TEM results.

Keywords: Elongated NCs, swift heavy ion irradiation, angle-dependent SAXS measurements.
PACS: 61.72.Ww, 61.46.Hk, 61.80.Jh, 61.10.Eq

INTRODUCTION

The accurate determination of nanocrystal (NC) size distributions has become fundamental, for many technological properties of nanoscale materials depend on their dimensions[1]. For this report, we have utilized both transmission electron microscopy (TEM) and small-angle X-ray scattering (SAXS) for the analysis of oriented non-spherical particles embedded in a matrix. Taking advantage of the well established models for the SAXS analysis of spherical particles[2], we demonstrate the possibility of determining the major and minor dimensions of rod-shaped NCs by the separate analysis of selected angular sectors of the detector. Only a few corrections are required to the spherical model to recover the dimensions of the major and minor axes of the NCs, as demonstrated by the excellent agreement between SAXS and TEM results[3].

EXPERIMENTAL

Pt NCs formed in 2 μm SiO_2 films by ion implantation (4.5 MeV Pt ions, 1×10^{17} cm^{-2}) and thermal annealing (1100 – 1300 °C for 1 h in forming gas) were irradiated with 185 MeV Au ions to a total fluence of 2×10^{14} cm^{-2}.

CP1092, Synchrotron Radiation in Materials Science: 6th International Conference, edited by R. Magalhaes-Paniago
© 2009 American Institute of Physics 978-0-7354-0625-4/09/$25.00

SAXS measurements were carried out at the ChemMatCARS beamline of the Advanced Photon Source. Measurements were performed in transmission mode with the sample surface normal oriented at angles from 0 to 45° relative to the photon beam.

RESULTS AND DISCUSSION

Figure 1 shows TEM micrographs of Pt NCs before and after swift heavy ion irradiation (SHII).

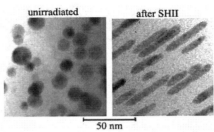

Figure 1 – TEM micrographs of Pt nanocrystals before and after SHII (185 MeV, 2×10^{14} cm^{-2}).

The aligned nature of the elongated NCs enabled the evaluation of both NC dimensions using SAXS. By varying the sample orientation relative to the beam direction, the scattering intensity collected by the detector was no longer isotropic, including significant differences in the intensity along the horizontal and vertical axes due to the non spherical nature of the elongated NCs. Selected angular sectors of the detector were integrated and analyzed separately, resulting in the individual evaluation of both the minor and major axes of the rod-like shaped NCs, as shown in Fig. 2.

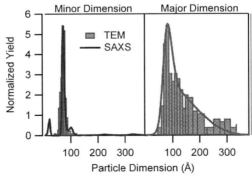

Figure 2 – Minor and major dimensions of elongated Pt NCs from TEM and SAXS. The right panel shows the projected major dimension at 45°.

CONCLUSIONS

Using our approach allowed the analysis of the SAXS spectra by means of existing methods (like maximum entropy), assuming spherical particles whose diameters correspond to the minor and major axes of the elongated NCs. The resulting diameter distributions of the Pt NCs are in excellent agreement with TEM analysis.

REFERENCES

1. E. Roduner *Chem. Soc. Rev.* 2006, 35, 583-592.
2. A. Guinier and G. Fournet, *Small-Angle Scattering of X-Rays.* 1955, New York: John Wiley and sons.
3   R. Giulian, P. Kluth, L. L. Araujo, D. J. Sprouster, A. P. Byrne, D. J. Cookson, and M. C. Ridgway *Phys. Rev. B* 2008, 78, 125413.

Structure analyses for Er-doped SiO$_2$ fibers (EDFs) by X-ray scattering, XAFS, and MD simulation.

Yoshihiro Saito*, Junji Iihara, Koji Yamaguchi, Tetsuya Haruna, and Hiroyuki Inoue[1].

Sumitomo Electric Industries, LTD. 1, Taya-cho, Sakae-ku, Yokohama, 244-8588, Japan
ysaito@sei.co.jp, junji-iihara@sei.co.jp, yamaguchi-koji@sei.co.jp, haruna-tetsuya@sei.co.jp
[1]Iinstitute of Industrial Science, University of Tokyo, inoue@iis.u-tokyo.ac.jp

Abstract. The structures of Er-doped SiO$_2$ fibers (EDFs) were analyzed by X-ray scattering, XAFS, and molecular dynamics (MD) simulations. The experiments and simulations have demonstrated that the Al-codoping expands Er-O distance and increases Er-O coordination number. These effects should cause a variation in the electric field around Er^{3+} in the SiO$_2$.

Keywords: Structure analyses, EDF, X-ray scattering, XAFS, MD simulation, RDF
PACS: 61.43.Fs

INTRODUCTION

EDF has been an indispensable device in the 1550nm-band optical amplifiers. Though aluminum (Al) is an effective co-dopant to broaden and flatten the bandwidth, its detailed mechanism is still unclear. We have investigated the mechanism, using X-ray scattering, XAFS and MD simulations.

EXPERIMENT AND SIMULATIONS

EDFs of different Al concentrations were fabricated by ordinary fiber manufacturing method. Then, the outer layers were etched to extract the Er-doped cores, which were finally ground into powders (see Figure 1). X-ray scattering spectra were measured by step-scanning of a scintillation counter. XAFS spectra near Er L$_{III}$-edge were obtained by fluorescence method. MD simulations were performed using optimized Born-Mayer type 2-body interatomic potentials. From the simulated structure models, total and partial radial distribution functions (RDFs) were calculated.

CP1092, *Synchrotron Radiation in Materials Science: 6th International Conference,* edited by R. Magalhaes-Paniago
© 2009 American Institute of Physics 978-0-7354-0625-4/09/$25.00

RESULTS

Figure 1 shows the total RDFs obtained from the X-ray scattering measurements. The small amount of Al-doping has been confirmed to slightly affect the RDFs that mainly reflect SiO_2 amorphous network. Figure 2 shows the results of the XAFS measurements. It has been found that the Al-doping expands the Er-O distance by approximately 0.03nm and that the higher Al concentration leads to the larger Er-O coordination number. Figures 1 and 2 also show the simulated RDFs, which have been confirmed to reproduce the trends obtained by the experiments.

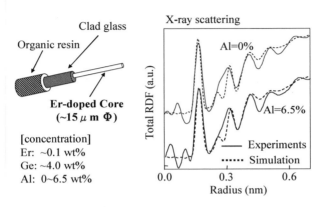

Figure 1 – Illustration of EDF specimen (left) and total RDFs from X-ray scattering and MD simulation (right).

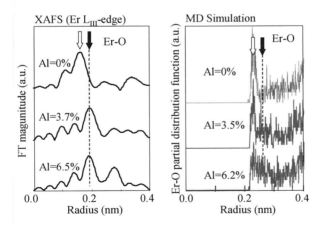

Figure 2 – RDFs from Er L_{III}-edge XAFS (left) and simulated partial distribution functions of Er-O (right). (Note that Ge and Er concentrations in simulations differ a little bit from ones in X-ray experiments.)

Al=0%   Al=6.5%

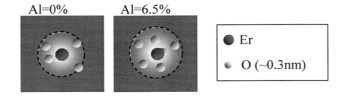

Er

O (~0.3nm)

Figure 3 – Examples of simulated EDF model. Dashed lines indicate averaged Er-O distances within 0.3nm.

DISCUSSION

The Er-O distance expansion and coordination number increase, as shown in Figure 3, are thought to cause the bandwidth broadening and flattening. The structure change should lead to a variation in the electric field around Er^{3+} and in the Stark levels of Er 4f orbitals. We are now simulating the optical emission wavelength and transition probability from each structure, in order to clarify the comprehensive mechanism.

ACKNOWLEDGMENTS

The X-ray experiments were done at SPring-8 with the approval of Japan Synchrotron Radiation Research Institute (JASRI) (Proposal No.: C03B16B2-4003-N, C04A16B2-4030-N, C04B16B2-4030-N, C05A16B2-4030-N, 2005B0799, C05A16BXU-3010-N). The authors also wish to thank Dr. Masugu Sato of JASRI for data processing program of X-ray scattering.

REFERENCES

T. Haruna et al: Optics Express, 14(23) (2006) 11036

Inelastic X-ray Scattering Studies of Zeolite Collapse

G. Neville Greaves*[1], Florian Kargl[1], David Ward[1], Peter Holliman[2] and Florian Meneau[3]

Centre for Advanced Functional Materials and Devices
[1]*Institute of Mathematics and Physics, Aberystwyth University, Aberystwyth SY23 3BZ UK;*
gng@aber.a.uk, ffk@aber.ac.uk, djw77@cam.ac.uk
[2]*College of Physical and Applied Sciences, Bangor University, Bangor LL57 2UW UK*
p.j.holliman@bangor.ac.uk
[3]*SOLEIL, Orme des Merisiers, Bâtiment A, Saint Aubin, BP 48, 91192, Gif sur Yvette Cedex, France*
florian.meneau@synchrotron-soleil.fr

Abstract. *In situ* inelastic x-ray scattering (IXS) experiments have been used to probe heterogeneity and deformability in zeolte Y as this thermally collapses to a high density amorphous (HDA) alumino-silicate phase. The Landau-Placzek ratio R_{LP} falls slowly as amorphisation advances, increasing in the later stages of collapse clearly showing how homogeneity improves non-linearly − behaviour linked closely with the decline in molar volume V_{Molar}. The Brillouin frequency ω_Q also decreases with amorphisation in a similar fashion, signifying a non-uniform decrease in the speed of sound v_l. All of these changes with zeolite amorphisation infer formation of an intermediate low density amorphous (LDA) phase. This low entropy or "perfect glass" has mechanical properties which are closer to the zeolite rather to the HDA glass − notably a very small value of Poisson's Ratio signifying unusually low resistance to deformation.

Keywords: Synchrotron radiation, materials science
PACS: 81.00.00

INTRODUCTION

Inelastic X-ray scattering probes the elastic constants of solids and liquids incorporated in the speed of sound $v_l = \omega_Q/Q$, as well as any inhomogeneity present registered in the non-ergodicty factor, $f_0 = R_{LP}/(1+R_{LP})$ [1]. R_{LP} is the Landau-Placzek Ratio which compares the area of the elastic Rayleigh line with the Brillouin doublet area. Amorphisation occurs when thermobaric stress overcomes periodic order [2] and zeolites become susceptible to amorphisation once dehydrated [3]. Evidence for an intermediate low density amorphous (LDA) phase has been inferred from collapse dynamics. Fig. 1 compares amorphisation and conventional melt quenching routes to the glass transition T_g by extending the Angell plot $\log \eta$ v T_g/T into the glassy state [3]. The steeper slopes at T_g for conventional melts contrast with the much shallower slopes encountered during zeolite collapse. These gentler gradients point to the existence of super strong liquids and below T_g to super rigid glasses. We have turned to inelastic x-

CP1092, *Synchrotron Radiation in Materials Science: 6th International Conference*, edited by R. Magalhaes-Paniago
© 2009 American Institute of Physics 978-0-7354-0625-4/09/$25.00

ray scattering (IXS) to identify the mechanical properties and degree of homogeneity of this new type of glass.

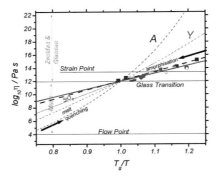

Figure 1. Angell plots of amuminosilicate melts A and Y compared to the stronger SiO_2 and the super strong liquids controlling the collapse of zeolite A and zeolite Y.

EXPERIMENTS

Experiments were performed on ID16 at the ESRF. Na Zeolite Y was amorphised for increasing times at 800°C and the temperature reduced at each stage to 600°C with measurements being made *in situ* at a wavevector value Q of 0.2Å^{-1}.

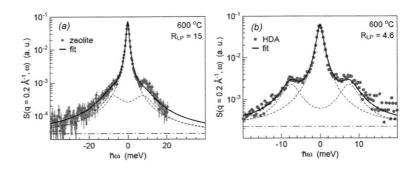

Figure 2. *In situ* IXS spectra for Na zeolite Y (a) and the HDA glass $Na_7Al_7Si_{17}O_{48}$ (b).

RESULTS AND DISCUSSION

In situ IXS spectra for Na zeolite Y and for the corresponding glass are shown in Fig. 2. The dashed curves show the deconvolution of the Rayleigh singlet from the Brillouin doublet and the satisfactory fit to the measured spectra.

Both the Landau-Placzek ratio R_{LP} and Brillouin frequency ω_Q as well as V_{Molar} are far greater for the zeolite than for the HDA glass. Moreover, as a function of amorphisation, V_{Molar} falls non-linearly between the zeolite and the HDA glass as shown in Fig. 3. In particular the LDA phase can be identified with the point where the decrease in V_{Molar} accelerates to the final high density HDA phase. The speed of sound v_l also falls non-uniformly as the zeolite collapses but the stiffness coefficient C_{11} which is proportional to v_l^2/V_{Molar} stays almost constant throughout. By comparison though the shear modulus G drops sharply as the HDA phase is approached mirroring the decline in V_{Molar}. The isothermal bulk modulus B on the other hand,

$$B = (3C_{11} - 4G)/3 \tag{1}$$

rises abruptly and so the ratio B/G rises, as a result of which there is a significant rise in Poisson's Ratio υ_P where

$$\upsilon_P = [3(B/G) - 2]/[6(B/G + 2)] \tag{2}.$$

In particular Poisson's Ratio is estimated to be 0.20 for the HDA glass compared to 0.17 for silica and 0.24 for diamond, making the alumino-silicate glass similarly deformable. Zeolite Y on the other hand is far less rigid with a value of $B/G \leq 2/3$ for which $\upsilon_P \leq 0$, bringing this microporous crystal into the class of auxetic materials. Because of its similar B/G ratio, Poisson's Ratio for the LDA glass is estimated to be 0.06 making it distinct from the final HDA glass, and one of the least deformable glasses so far reported [2].

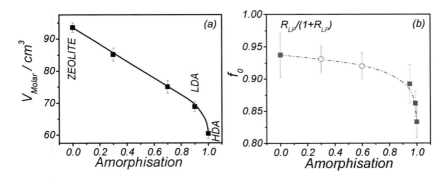

Figure 3. (a) Decline in V_{Molar} with aorphisation of zeolite Y, identifying the intermediate LDA phase. (b) Corresponding fall in f_0 measured from inelastic X-ray scattering.

Whilst υ_P increases significantly during the collapse of zeolite Y, so does the strength of Brillouin scattering (Fig. 2). The result is that R_{LP} drops sharply from ~15 in the zeolite to ~5 in the HDA glass (Fig. 2) and with it the non-ergodicity factor f_0. The fall of f_0 accelerates between LDA and HDA as shown in Fig. 3(b), revealing similarities to the two-stage process found in the decline of V_{Molar} during amorphisation (Fig. 3(a)). Accordingly both the zeolite and the LDA are characterised by higher non-ergodicity compared to the final HDA glass.

In the limit $Q{\rightarrow}0$ the self part of the non-ergodicity factor f_0 can be equated to the Debye-Waller factor familiar in crystallography [1,2]. Consequently the starting zeolite and the intermediate LDA phase are less homogeneous than the final HDA glass. The origins of inhomogeneity in microporous crystals were found in early EXAFS experiments on zeolites where considerable static disorder was identified in the local environments of charge compensating cations like Ni [4]. Subsequently these distortions were associated with stationary Rigid Unit Modes deduced from Constaint Theory [5]. Indeed low frequency vibrations have now been identified in zeolites using inelastic neutron scattering [6] and are also reported at this conference in new infrared spectra for zeolite A and zeolite Y [7]. The frequencies of these oscillations occur in the THz range in the vicinity of the Boson Peak which characterises the glassy state [2]. They are however much stronger in zeolites compared to melt-quenched glasses [6]. Moreover, as the intensity of these low frquency vibrations remain strong up to the LDA-HDA transition [6], it is reasonable to conclude that the standing wave distortions characteristic of the zeolite will also be maintained in the LDA glass, the amorphous structure homogenising once the HDA glass forms.

In summary the LDA phase represents a new type of glass whose aperiodic structure is toplogically similar to the precursor microporous crystals [2]. At the same time it incorporates deformability (low Poisson ratio) and inhomogeneity (high non-ergodicity) which is also characteristic of the starting zeolite.

ACKNOWLEDGMENTS

We would like to thank the Higher Education Funding Council of Wales for support through the Centre for Advanced Functional Materials and Devices, and the Science and Technology Facilities Council for providing access to the ESRF.

REFERENCES

1. T. Scopigno, G. Ruocco, F. Sette and G. Monaco, *Science* **302**, 849 (2003)
2. G.N. Greaves and S. Sen, *Adv. Phys.* **56**, 1 (2007)
3. G.N.Greaves, F. Meneau, A. Sapelkin, L.M. Colyer, I. Ap Gwynn, S. Wade and G. Sankar, *NatureMaterials* **2**, 62 (2003)
4. E. Dooryhee, A.T. Steel, P.J. Maddox, J.M. Thomas, C.R.A. Catlow, J.W. Couves, G.N. Greaves and K.P. Townsend *J. Phys. Chem.* **95**, 1229 (1991)
5. K.D. Hammonds, H. Deng, V. Heine and M.T. Dove *Phys. Rev. Lett.* **78**, 3701 (1997)
6. G.N. Greaves, F. Meneau, O. Majérus, D. Jones and J.Taylor *Science* **308**, 1299 (2005)
7. M. Bahou, L. Wen, H O.Moser, G. N. Greaves and F. Kargl – SRMS-6

Swift Heavy Ion Irradiation of Cobalt Nanoparticles

D. J. Sprouster [a] *, R. Giulian[a], C. S. Schnohr[a], P. Kluth[a], L. L. Araujo[a], A. P. Byrne[b], G. J. Foran[c], and M. C. Ridgway[a]

[a]*Department of Electronic Materials Engineering, Australian National University, Canberra ACT 0200, Australia*
[b]*College of Science Frank Fenner Building, Australian National University, ACT 0200 Australia*
[c]*Australian Nuclear Science and Technology Organisation, Menai, NSW 2234, Australia*
* Corresponding author: djs109@rsphysse.anu.edu.au

Abstract. It is well known that the electronic energy loss released by swift heavy ions can cause considerable atomic movement in various solids. Here, we present a study of the effects of swift heavy ion irradiation on Co nanoparticles embedded within a silica host matrix. The evolution of the Co nanoparticle crystal phase, structural properties, shape and size has been characterized using a combination of x-ray absorption spectroscopy and transmission electron microscopy. An FCC-to-HCP phase transformation is observed at low fluences, while higher fluences result in significant changes in the short range order and NP shape. After an incubation fluence the nanoparticles deform into ellipsoids, preferentially aligned parallel to the incident beam direction. The threshold diameter for elongation was comparable to the saturation value of the ellipsoid width. We correlate this saturation value with the diameter of the molten track induced in amorphous silica by swift heavy ion irradiation.

Keywords: Co, NPs, XAS, TEM, phase transformation, swift heavy ion irradiation.
PACS: 61.05.cj, 61.46.Hk

INTRODUCTION

Recently swift heavy ion irradiation (SHII) has been shown to induce a shape transform in embedded nanoparticles (NPs). Initially, the NPs are spherical and transform to ellipsoids with their major axis parallel to the direction of the incident ion beam [1-3]. In the present study, x-ray absorption spectroscopy (XAS) and transmission electron microscopy (TEM) are employed to structurally characterize the evolution of Co NPs embedded within a silica host matrix, before and after SHII.

EXPERIMENTAL

1.4 MeV Co ions were implanted to a fluence of 3×10^{17} ions/cm^2 into 2μm thick SiO$_2$ thermally grown on a Si (100) substrate, yielding a Co peak concentration of 9 at. % (or ~ 3×10^{17} NPs/cm^3). The samples were subsequently annealed in flowing forming gas (5% H$_2$ + 95% N$_2$) for 1 h at a temperature of 1100 °C to induce

CP1092, *Synchrotron Radiation in Materials Science: 6th International Conference*, edited by R. Magalhaes-Paniago
© 2009 American Institute of Physics 978-0-7354-0625-4/09/$25.00

precipitation and nanocrystal growth. The resulting NP volume-weighted average diameter was ~170 Å.

Samples were then irradiated with 185, MeV ^{197}Au ions in a wide fluence region of 10^{12}-10^{14} ions/cm^2 at normal incidence. The electronic stopping power and range of 185 MeV ions in SiO$_2$ were calculated by the TRIM [4] code to be 17.63 keV/nm and 19.18 μm respectively. The range of the ions is well beyond the NPs position in the SiO$_2$ matrix to stem any Au impurity effects. The size and shape of the NPs was characterized by X-TEM, performed on a Phillips CM300 microscope operating at 300 kV.

A unique sample preparation method was used to isolate the thin SiO$_2$ layer containing Co NPs for the synchrotron measurements. This was achieved by the removal of the Si substrate through mechanical grinding and selective wet chemical etching with KOH. Multiple thin Co NP rich SiO$_2$ layers were then suspended between two pieces of Kapton tape. The technique enables higher resolution measurements as significant NP material can be concentrated within a sample holder without scattering from the Si substrate.

Fluorescence mode XAS measurements were performed at beamline 20-B of the Photon Factory, Japan. Samples were measured at the Co K edge (7709 eV) at 15 K to minimize thermal vibrations. Crystallographic phase fractions were determined by fitting a linear combination of metallic and oxide standards to the x-ray absorption near edge spectra (XANES). Structural parameters were determined from the extended x-ray absorption fine structure (EXAFS) region using the non-linear least squared fitting code within IFEFFIT [5] for the first nearest neighbor shell. Complete details of the data analysis procedures are described in reference [6].

RESULTS

The XANES spectra for the 185 MeV SHII sample set are displayed in Figure 1. The NPs are initially in an FCC phase and after a low fluence of ~ 1 x 10^{13} ions/cm^2 transform to the HCP phase. Higher fluence irradiations results in an increase in the number of Co atoms in an oxidized environment. The crystallographic fractions determined from the linear combination fitting of the XANES region are shown in Figure 3 a) as a function of SHII fluence. The phase transformation has also been observed for smaller (130 Å) NPs and is attributed to the SHII induced strain build up the host SiO^2 matrix [7]. The metal-to-oxide transformation is attributed to the progressive dissolution of the NPs into the matrix (or, equivalently, into an oxidized environment).

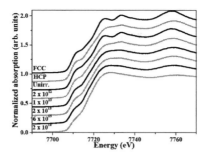

FIGURE 1. XANES spectra for foil standards, unirradiated and selected irradiated NPs offset for clarity.

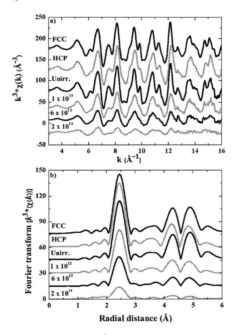

FIGURE 2. a) Background subtracted k^3-weighted EXAFS spectra (offset) for bulk standards, unirradiated and irradiated NPs standards and b) the corresponding phase corrected Fourier-transformed EXAFS spectra (also offset for comparison).

The evolution of the EXAFS signal with SHII fluence is shown in Figure 2. Upon SHII significant changes in both the NP EXAFS amplitude and the FT peak amplitudes are observable. The reduction in amplitude with ion fluence is indicative of a reduced coordination and / or an increase in the Debye-waller factor (disorder). The evolution of the structural parameters (coordination number, bondlength and Debye-Waller factor) calculated from the EXAFS analysis is shown in Figure 3 as a function of SHII fluence. An increase in the Debye-Waller factor and decrease in both the coordination number and bondlength were calculated for increasing ion fluence.

This behavior is consistent with the increase in the number of small NPs with ion fluence observed with TEM and is attributable to both the increasing surface-area-to-volume ratio for decreasing NP size [8] and the dissolution of Co atoms into the matrix. The latter has a significant effect on the coordination number and further work is in progress to accurately account for the fraction of Co atoms dissolved in the matrix [9].

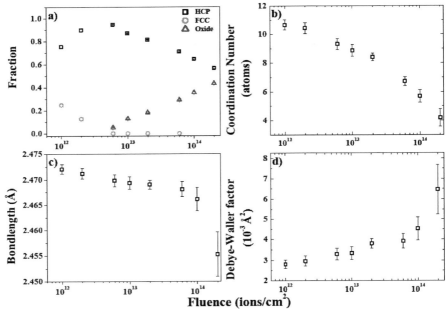

FIGURE 3. a) XANES fractions and calculated structural parameters from the EXAFS analysis; b) coordination number; c) bondlength; d) Debye-Waller factor as a function of 185MeV SHII fluence

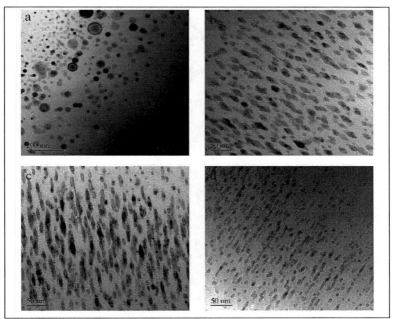

Figure 4. TEM images showing the evolution of NP shape as a function of SHII Fluence. a) Unirradiated; b) 2 x 10 [13]; c) 6 x 10 [13]; d) 2 x 10[14]. Arrows indicate ion beam direction

Figure 4 shows TEM images of the evolution of NP shape, as function of SHII fluence. Spherical NPs below a minimum diameter (~65 Å) remained spherical in shape and are progressively dissolved into the matrix with higher fluence. NPs above this minimum diameter transform into ellipsoids aligned along the incident ion beam direction. The ellipsoids minor dimension (or width) saturates at ~70 Å as shown in Figure 4. Size distributions of the minor dimension from TEM counting and small angle x-ray scattering (not shown here for brevity) are also very narrow. The volume fraction of the small spherical NPs also increases with ion fluence due to the fragmentation of the large NPs. The major dimensions of the ellipsoids are quite broad and are consistent with that of the unirradiated spherical NPs. The saturation value of the ellipsoids width was well correlated with the diameter of the molten track in SiO_2 induced by SHII (~107 Å) [10]. Such results are consistent with a shape transformation driven by nanoparticle melting and redistribution of material within the ion track [11,12].

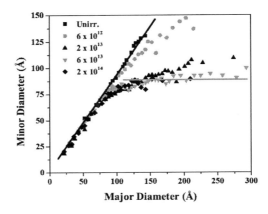

FIGURE 5. Major and minor dimensions measured by TEM as a function SHII fluence.

CONCLUSIONS

We have employed XAS and TEM to characterize changes in the crystal phase, structural properties, shape and the size of embedded Co NPs induced by swift heavy-ion irradiation. An FCC-to-HCP phase transformation was complete at low fluence and attributed to the build-up of ion beam induced strain within the SiO_2 matrix. At high fluence, an increase in the fraction of Co atoms dispersed in an oxidized environment was calculated and is attributed to the gradual dissolution of the NPs. An increase in the Debye-Waller factor (or disorder) and decrease in both the coordination number and bondlength were calculated from the EXAFS analysis. The structural trends calculated for the NPs with increasing SHII fluence are consistent with the increasing surface-area-to-volume ratios for the small NPs that increase in number with ion fluence. NPs below a threshold diameter were found to remain spherical upon irradiation and progressively dissolve into the matrix. NPs above this threshold transform into aligned ellipsoids oriented parallel to the incident beam direction. The width of the ellipsoids saturates at a value comparable to the threshold diameter for spherical nanoparticle elongation. This saturation value of ellipsoid width is correlated with the diameter of the molten track induced in amorphous SiO_2 by swift heavy-ion irradiation. The shape transformation of the Co NPs presented here is consistent with the elongation of a once-spherical molten nanoparticle confined to the diameter of the molten silica track.

ACKNOWLEDGMENTS

This work was financially supported by the Australian Synchrotron Research Program and the Australian Research Council. We thank C.J. Glover, E. Frain and I. McKerracher for helpful discussions.

REFERENCES

1   C. D'Orleans, J. P. Stoquert, C. Estournes, C. Cerruti, J. J. Grob, J. L. Guille, F. Haas, D. Muller, and M. Richard-Plouet, *Phys. Rev. B* **67**, 220101 (2003).
2   S. Roorda, T. van Dillen, A. Polman, C. Graf, A. van Blaaderen, and B. J. Kooi, *Adv. Mater.* **16**, 235 (2004).
3   T. van Dillen, A. van Blaaderen, and A. Polman, *Mater. Today* 7, 40 (2004).
4   J. F. Ziegler, J. P. Beirsack, and U. Littmark, The Stopping and Range of Ions in Matter (Pergamon Press, New York, 1985).
5   M. Newville, *J. Synchrotron Radiat.* 8, 322 (2001).
6   D. Sprouster, B. Johannessen, R. Giulian, Z. Hussain, L. L. Araujo, P. Kluth, D. J. Cookson, G. J. Foran, and M. C. Ridgway, *unpublished* (2008).
7   D. Sprouster, R. Giulian, B. Johannessen, C. S. Schnohr, L. L. Araujo, P. Kluth, A. P. Byrne, G. J. Foran, and M. C. Ridgway, *Nanotechnology* submitted (2008).
8   B. Johannessen, P. Kluth, C. J. Glover, G. D. Azevedo, D. J. Llewellyn, G. J. Foran, and M. C. Ridgway, *J. Appl. Phys.* **98**, 024307 (2005).
9   D. J. Sprouster, R. Giulian, L. L. Araujo, C. S. Schnohr, P. Kluth, D. J. Llewellyn, A. P. Byrne, G. J. Foran, D. J. Cookson, and M. C. Ridgway, *unpublished* (2008).
10 P. Kluth, C. S. Schnohr, O. H. Pakarinen, F. Djurabekova, D. J. Sprouster, R. Giulian, M. C. Ridgway, A. P. Byrne, C. Trautmann, D. J. Cookson, K. Nordlund, and M. Toulemonde, *Phys. Rev. Lett.* **101**, 175503 (2008).
11 A. Koichi, W. Xiaomin, F. Makoto, T. Junji, A. Hirohiko, O. Yoshimichi, and K. Tetsuro, *Phys. Rev. B* **78**, 054102 (2008).
12 M. C. Ridgway, P. Kluth, R. Giulian, D. J. Sprouster, L. L. Araujo, C. S. Schnohr, D. J. Llewellyn, A. P. Byrne, G. J. Foran, and D. J. Cookson, *Nucl. Instrum. Methods Phys. Res. B.* in press (2008).

Fundamental Interactions at Oxide Surfaces: Understanding Novel Dye-sensitised Solar Cells

Wendy R Flavell[a], Andrew G Thomas[a], Asurasinghe R Kumarasinghe[a], Christopher P Chatwin[a], Sunil Patel[b] Vinod Dhanak[b], George Miller[b], Michael Grätzel[c] and Roland Hengerer[c]

[a]The Photon Science Institute, The University of Manchester, Alan Turing Building, Oxford Rd, Manchester, M13 9PL, UK.
[b]STFC Daresbury Laboratory, Warrington, Cheshire WA4 4 AD, UK.
[c]Swiss Federal Institute of Technology, Laboratory for Photonics and interfaces, Chemin des Alambics, CH-1015, Lausanne, Switzerland.

Abstract. Studies using synchrotron radiation (SR) to probe the electronic structure, bonding and carrier dynamics at photovoltaic surfaces and interfaces are described. This includes a study of the growth of the p-type inorganic semiconductor CuI on n-type TiO_2 nanoparticulate and single-crystal anatase surface using SR photoemission spectroscopy. This is complemented by NEXAFS (near-edge X-ray absorption fine structure) studies of the adsorption of model sensitising dyes at this interface. The data show that the interface between p-CuI and single crystal and nanocrystalline anatase-phase n-TiO_2 is a type II heterojunction interface, with significant band-bending, contrasting with the 'flat-band' energy level line-up normally assumed for such cells. NEXAFS is used to derive a canted, roughly upright geometry for BINA (bi-isonicotinic acid, a part of the dye molecule structure) adsorbed at the anatase surface.

Keywords: Dye-sensitised solid state solar cell, photoemission, n-TiO_2/p-CuI heterojunction, interface energy level diagram, band-bending, near-edge X-ray absorption fine structure (NEXAFS), bi-isonicotinic acid (BINA).
PACS: 73.22.-f,73.20.At,73.30.+y, 79.60.-i, 79.60.Dp, 79.60.Jv.

INTRODUCTION

The solid-state dye-sensitised solar cell offers a potentially cost-effective and easy to manufacture light-to-electrical energy conversion system [1]. Despite intense activity in the development and optimisation of new solar cells, there are rather few direct measurements of the energy level line-up at the heterojunctions at the heart of these devices with which to guide this process. Fundamental studies using synchrotron radiation (SR) to probe the electronic structure, bonding and carrier dynamics at photovoltaic surfaces and interfaces are described here.

EXPERIMENTAL

Photoemission and NEXAFS measurements were carried out at beamlines 6.1 and 5U.1 at the UK Synchrotron Radation Source (SRS) at Daresbury UK. The TiO_2/CuI

CP1092, *Synchrotron Radiation in Materials Science: 6th International Conference*, edited by R. Magalhaes-Paniago
© 2009 American Institute of Physics 978-0-7354-0625-4/09/$25.00

heterojunction at the heart of the solid-state cell was created *in situ* in UHV by gettering CuI onto clean anatase TiO_2 (101) and as-presented nanoparticulate anatase surfaces. The coverage of CuI was estimated from XPS and Auger measurements. In separate experiments, the orientation of the light-sensitising dye (the so-called 'N3' or Ru bipyridyl dye) at the surface of anatase was probed by absorbing BINA (bi-isonicotinic acid) – the dye ligand – at single crystal anatase (101) and (001) surfaces.

RESULTS AND DISCUSSION

Valence band photoemission data was used to monitor the introduction of a new density of states within the band gap of TiO_2 as a result of the growth of CuI. The core and valence level features were found to shift as a function of CuI deposition. These shifts, when referenced to bulk TiO_2 [2] and CuI [3] samples, suggest that the interface between p-CuI and single crystal and nanocrystalline anatase-phase n-TiO_2 is a type II heterojunction interface, with significant band-bending. The energy level diagram resulting from the photoemission experiments for nanocrystalline anatase with around 6 Å of CuI deposited is shown in Figure 1.

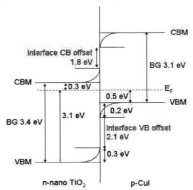

FIGURE 1. Band energy alignment at the heterojunction interface for an as-presented nanoparticulate anatase-phase n-TiO_2 thin film (of average particle size 7.3 nm) and p-CuI. The diagram shows the alignment after 90 minutes' CuI deposition (equivalent to around 6 Å layer thickness if uniformly deposited). The diagram is constructed using the experimentally observed core level binding energy shifts for the anatase TiO_2 substrate and the CuI overlayer, the measured valence band maxima for nanoparticulate TiO_2 and CuI, and also using reported bandgap (BG) values for nanoparticulate anatase TiO_2 and CuI [3]. 'VBM' and 'CBM' indicate the valence band (VB) maxima and conduction band (CB) minima respectively.

This result contrasts with the 'flat-band' energy level line-up normally assumed for such cells; this assumption originates in an expectation that in a nanoparticulate semiconductor, the nanoparticles are too small to allow a depletion layer to be maintained to support the surface band-bending [4]. In contrast, TiO_2 is grossly non-stoichiometric, and the defect concentrations probed by photoemission give an estimated depletion layer depth of 1.6 nm, smaller than the radius of the nanoparticles (3.6 nm on average) [3]. The correct measurement of the energy level line-up at this junction is crucial, as the dye-sensitiser is chosen to have energy levels that are optimised relative to those of the n- and p-type components of the junction.

The geometry of the N3 dye-sensitiser at the anatase surface in the solar cell is determined largely by the bi-isonicotinic acid (BINA) ligands. A combination of C K-edge and N K-edge measurements was used to determine the orientation of the ligand at both the anatase (101) and (001) surfaces [5]. This was supported by calculations using the StoBe codes [6]. Experimental and calculated C K-edge NEXAFS, together with the resulting molecular orientation, are shown in Figure 2.

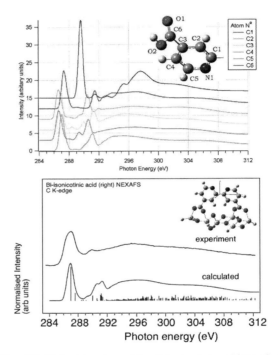

FIGURE 2. Use of StoBe to determine origin of electronic transitions of a single BINA molecule in experimental NEXAFS spectra. The upper panel shows the NEXAFS spectrum for transitions arising from each of the individual C atoms labelled in the inset. (Note the oscillator strengths are not to scale in this panel). The lower part of figure shows the experimental NEXAFS spectrum compared to a calculated NEXAFS spectrum of BINA on a single layer cluster of the TiO_2 (101) surface. The inset shows the molecular model used to produce the theoretical NEXAFS spectrum with the BINA molecule in the experimentally determined orientation and bonding site.

Consistent with the geometry determined for the rutile (110) surface [7], the molecule is adsorbed in a bidentate geometry, with the phenyl rings tilted around 20 ° either side of the surface normal. For the (001) surface a rather different result is found; the measured tilt to the macroscopic surface is around 53 °. This is thought to be influenced by the complex (1x4) reconstruction of this surface, which is microfacetted [5].

CONCLUSIONS

These measurements provide the first direct measurement of the energy level diagram for a solid-state TiO_2-based photovoltaic junction. This result contrasts with the 'flat-band' energy level line-up normally assumed for such cells. NEXAFS is used to derive a canted, roughly upright geometry for BINA (bi-isonicotinic acid, a part of the dye molecule structure) adsorbed at the anatase surface.

ACKNOWLEDGMENTS

Funding from the UK research councils EPSRC and STFC is gratefully acknowledged. We also thank Petter Persson for generous assistance in implementing the StoBe codes.

REFERENCES

1. see e.g. M Grätzel, *Inorg. Chem.* **44,** 6841-6851 (2004).
2. A.G. Thomas, W.R. Flavell, A.K. Mallick, A.R. Kumarasinghe, D.Tsoutsou, N. Khan, C. Chatwin, S. Rayner and G.C. Smith R.L. Stockbauer, S. Warren, T.K. Johal, S.Patel and D. Holland, A. Taleb and F. Wiame, *Phys. Rev. B* **75**, 035105(12) (2007).
3. A R Kumarasinghe, W R Flavell, A G Thomas, A K Mallick, D Tsoutsou, C Chatwin, S Rayner, P Kirkham, S Warren, S Patel, P Christian, P O'Brien, M Grätzel and R Hengerer, *J. Chem. Phys.* **127**, 114703(14) (2007).
4. see e.g. M Grätzel, *J. Photochem. Photobiol. A*. **164**, 3-14 (2004).
5. A G Thomas, W R Flavell, C Chatwin, S Rayner, D Tsoutsou, A R Kumarasinghe, D Brete, T K Johal, S Patel and J Purton, *Surf. Sci.*, **592**, 159-168 (2005).
6. K. Hermann and L.G.M. Pettersson, M.E. Casida, C. Daul, A. Goursot, A. Koester, E. Proynov, A. St-Amant, and D.R. Salahub. Contributing authors: V. Carravetta, H. Duarte, N. Godbout, J. Guan, C. Jamorski, M. Leboeuf, V. Malkin, O. Malkina, M. Nyberg, L. Pedocchi, F. Sim, L. Triguero, and A. Vela, StoBe Software, 2002.
7. L Patthey, H Rensmo, P Persson, K Westermark, L Vayssieres, A Stahans, P A Bruhweiler, H Siegbahn, S Lunell and N Martensson, *J. Chem. Phys.* **110**, 5913-5918 (1999).

Free-space Electromagnetic Metamaterials From The Far Infrared To The Visible

Herbert O. Moser[a], Linke Jian[a], Mohammed Bahou[a], B. Didier F. Casse[d],
Shenbaga M.P. Kalaiselvi[a], Gang Liu[a], Sivakumar M. Maniam[a], Pengda
Gu[a], Ao Chen[a], Sascha P. Heussler[a], Shahrain bin Mahmood[a], Li Wen[a],
Jin Au Kong[b,c](†), Hongsheng Chen[b,c], Xiangxiang Cheng[c], Bae-Ian Wu[b]

[a]*Singapore Synchrotron Light Source, National University of Singapore, 5 Research Link, Singapore 117603*
[b]*Research Laboratory of Electronics, Massachusetts Institute of Technology, Cambridge, Massachusetts 02139, USA*
[c]*The Electromagnetics Academy at Zhejiang University, Zhejiang University, Hangzhou 310058, China*
[d]*Dept. of Physics and Electronic Materials Research Institute, Northeastern University, Boston, USA*

Abstract. The development of electromagnetic metamaterials by micro/nanomanufacturing at SSLS has led to matrix-embedded or substrate-supported rod-split-ring-based samples reaching left-handed pass-bands at 216 THz or 1.39 μm and to free-space S-string bi-layer chips at 2.2 THz. Potential applications of metamaterials range from sub-wavelength resolution imaging over invisibility cloaking to advanced antennae and are relevant to fields including microscopy, lithography, electromagnetic shielding, and telecommunication.

Keywords: Metamaterials, terahertz, electromagnetism, micro/nanomanufacturing, rod-split-ring, S-string, free-standing
PACS: 41.20.Jb, 41.60.Ap, 42.25.Bs, 85.85.+j

INTRODUCTION

Stimulated by Veselago's [1] and Pendry's [2] seminal work, the development of electromagnetic metamaterials (EM^3) has surged during the past decade. EM^3 are characterized by both, dielectric permittivity ε and magnetic permeability μ being negative. Not naturally occurring, they are realized as artificial composites that feature a dense spatial distribution of small metallic unit elements which have a resonant response to an incoming electromagnetic wave within a certain frequency band. Critical for achieving μ<0, resonators might have various shapes all representing current loops and their inductances and capacitances. Pendry's first proposal of a nested double split-ring has become a workhorse, but other structures have also been developed, in particular, string-like metal arrangements like S [3] and Ω. The second criterion of ε<0 is fulfilled when the frequency of the magnetic resonator is smaller than the plasma frequency of the whole metal distribution. After the proof-of-principle experiment in the lower GHz frequency range by Smith et al. in 2000 [4], resonance frequencies were since driven higher by about 5 orders of magnitude into the THz range up to the visible red [5]. One of the reasons for this strong quest towards the infrared and visible spectral range is that some important potential applications of metamaterials are related to optics, in particular, in the IR and visible. Prominent examples include sub-wavelength resolution imaging and microscopy, and invisibility cloaking in which the electromagnetic wave is guided around the cloaking device such that it looks identical upstream and downstream. The development of the ever smaller metal structures needed for short wavelengths was enabled by micro/nanomanufacturing.

MICRO/NANOMANUFACTURING

The tools required to produce EM^3 for the infrared and visible include primary pattern generators such as e beam writer, laser direct writer, mask aligner for UV lithography, a synchrotron radiation beamline with an X-ray scanner for X-ray deep lithography (XRDL), electroplating, sputter deposition, auxiliary process equipment, and metrology. Details of the manufacturing processes used may be found in ref. [6].

The driving force behind SSLS' application of (deep) X-ray lithography to the manufacturing of EM^3 is the goal to be able to produce EM^3 in large quantities and high quality, finally justifying the use of the word material. SSLS has built both, rod-split-ring resonators covering a spectral range from about 1 THz to 216 THz, and S-string window-frame bi-layer chips above 2 THz. The latter are the first free-space metamaterials ever built. Fig. 1 shows examples of a Ni rod-split-ring structure

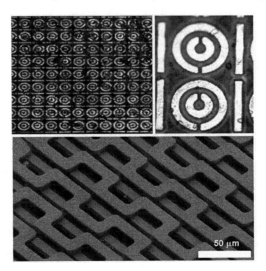

FIGURE 1. Ni rod-split- ring structure in bird's eye view and close-up. Outer diameter of outer ring 80 μm (top). Close-up of Au S-string free-space bi-layer chip (bottom), scale bar 50 μm.

embedded in an AZ P4620 resist matrix [7] and of a free-space window-frame S-string bi-layer chip [8]. In both cases, the left-handed pass-band is around 2 THz. Fig. 2

67

displays SSLS' record frequency rod-split-ring structure and a PMMA template for even higher frequencies around 700 THz or a wavelength of 425 nm. However, at these frequencies, the influence of intrinsic excitations of the metal used like surface

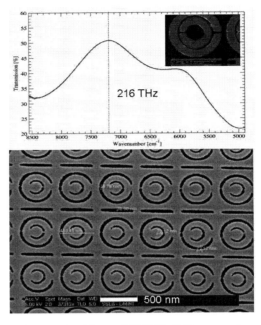

FIGURE 2. Au rod-split-ring sample with record 216 THz (1.39 µm wavelength) resonance, outer diameter 1.6 µm(top); PMMA template patterned by e beam for about 700 THz, scale bar 500 nm (bottom).

plasmon polaritons may limit the achievable frequency and must be taken into account.

RESULTS AND DISCUSSION

The spectral response of the samples is measured by means of Fourier transform interferometry with synchrotron infrared light using a Bruker IFS 66v/S FTIR. The incoming beam is linearly polarized. The sample can be inclined such as to vary the angle of incidence of the incoming beam which offers a way to vary magnetic field coupling to the resonance loop. Fig. 3 shows measured and simulated spectra of a free-space S-string bi-layer chip with Au S-strings suspended by a window-frame made from SU-8 resist. The spectra are characterized by two peaks at about 2.2 and 2.9 THz which decrease in amplitude and shift in frequency when the incidence angle is increased from 0° to 60°. The simulation of a few S-strings of the given geometry reproduces the general shape of two peaks rather well although there is a shift to higher frequencies by about 0.2 to 0.3 THz. The decrease of the peak height is less well reproduced as the real bi-layer chip has many strings while the simulation takes

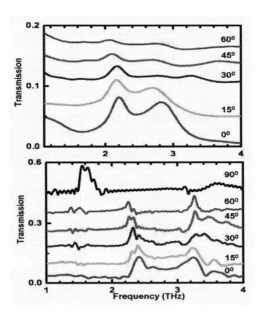

FIGURE 3. Measured (top) and simulated (bottom) spectra of free-space Au S-string bi-layer at a gap of 1.1 μm.

into account only five. A calculation to retrieve the effective parameters ε and μ has confirmed that the 2.2 THz pass-band is left-handed (not shown).

CONCLUSION

Encouraging progress was made with both, the matrix-embedded or substrate-supported rod-split-ring and the free-space S-string architecture. While rod-split-ring devices have nearly reached the visible, more work needs to be done on higher frequency S-strings. As a next goal, SSLS is aiming at >10 THz.

ACKNOWLEDGMENTS

Work partly performed at SSLS under DARPA HR0011-06-1-0030, NUS Core Support C-380-003-003-001, A*STAR/MOE RP 3979908M and A*STAR 12 105 0038 grants. JAK and HSC would also like to acknowledge the Chinese National Science Foundation under contract 60531020.

REFERENCES

1.   V.G. Veselago, *Sov. Phys. Usp.* **10**, 509(1968).

2. J.B. Pendry, A.J. Holden, D.J. Robbins, W.J. Stewart, *IEEE Trans. Microwave Theory Tech.* **47**, 2075(1999).
3. H.S. Chen, L.X. Ran, J.T. Huangfu, X.M. Zhang, K.S. Chen, T. Grzegorzyk, J.A. Kong, *Phys. Rev. E* **70**, 057605(2004).
4. D.R. Smith, W.J. Padilla, D.C. Vier, S.C. Nemat-Nasser, S. Schultz, *Phys. Rev. Lett.* **84**, 4184 (2000).
5. V. M. Shalaev, *Nature Photonics* **1**, 41(2007).
6. Linke Jian et al., this conference.
7. H.O. Moser, B.D.F. Casse, O. Wilhelmi, B.T. Saw, *Phys. Rev. Lett.* **94**, 063901(2005).
8. H.O. Moser, J.A. Kong, L.K. Jian, H.S. Chen, G. Liu, M. Bahou, S.M.P. Kalaiselvi, S.M. Maniam, X.X. Cheng, B.I. Wu, P.D. Gu, A. Chen, S.P. Heussler, Shahrain bin Mahmood, L. Wen, *Opt. Express* **16**, 13773-13780(2008).

Characterising density fluctuations in liquid yttria aluminates with small angle x-ray scattering

G. Neville Greaves[1], Martin C. Wilding[1], Quang Vu Van[*1], Odile Majérus[2] and Louis Hennet[3]

[1]Centre for Advanced Functional Materials and Devices
Institute of Mathematics and Physics, Aberystwyth University, Aberystwyth SY23 3BZ UK;
gng@aber.ac.uk, mbw@aber.ac.uk, qqv05@aber.ac.uk
[2]Ecole nationale Supérieure de Chemie de paris, 11 rue Pierre et marie Curies, 75231, Paris, France.
Odile-Majerus@enscp.fr
[3]CNRS-CRMHT, 1d avenue de la Recherche Scietifique, 45071 Orléans cedex 9, France.
hennet@cnrs-orleans.fr

Abstract. Small angle x-ray scattering (SAXS) has been measured in the wavevector range $0.01<Q<1\text{Å}^{-1}$ for supercooled yttria-alumina melts using a laser-heated aerodynamic furnace. SAXS intensity rises gradually with temperature reflecting density fluctuations deriving from isothermal compressibility. With decreasing Q a minimum is located close to 0.1Å^{-1} at the foot of the inter-atomic structure factor, below which SAXS rises, suggesting scatter from longer range fluctuating volumes.

Keywords: Materials Science, Synchrotron Radiation
PACS: 81.00.00

INTRODUCTION

The process of maintaining equilibrium in ergodic liquids at ambient pressure P and temperature T necessarily involves random fluctuations $\sqrt{\langle \Delta \rho^2 \rangle}$ in the average density ρ_0 in response to external stress. These fluctuations increase with T and are otherwise only a function of the compressibility of the liquid K_T,

$$V<\Delta\rho^2>/\rho_0^2=k_B T K_T \tag{1}$$

where V is the average volume of the spatially dispersed fluctuating elements [1]. In glass forming systems, as the temperature falls through the supercooled region, density fluctuations become frozen in at the glass transition temperature T_g. Random fluctuations in density in the liquid and glassy state introduce an additional contribution to the scattered intensity of x-rays at low wavevector Q, $I(Q)$, which can be measured in the limit as Q approaches zero, viz:

CP1092, Synchrotron Radiation in Materials Science: 6th International Conference, edited by R. Magalhaes-Paniago
© 2009 American Institute of Physics 978-0-7354-0625-4/09/$25.00

$$V <\Delta\rho^2 > / \rho_0^2 = S(0)/ \rho_0 = I(0)/(\rho_0 \sum_\alpha^N W_{\alpha\beta...}^2) \qquad (2)$$

where $\sum_\alpha^N W_{\alpha\beta...}^2$ is the average cross section for the different atoms present weighted according to the composition. The same fluctuations can also be detected from Brillouin scattering and Zarzycki used early SAXS and Brillouin data for silica glass to deduce that $V \sim 9 \cdot 10^3 \text{Å}^3$ at the glass transition, suggesting elements with an average size of around 10Å in radius fluctuating in density $\sqrt{\langle\Delta\rho^2\rangle}/\rho_0^2$ by around 1% [1]. T_g occurs around 1200K in silica and so eq. 1 points to a compressibility K_T of close to 80 10^{-6} MPa^{-1} in the supercooled liquid. This is three times the solid state value of 27 10^{-6} MPa^{-1} measured directly for silica under ambient conditions. This ratio for the liquid and solid silica compressibilities is surprisingly similar to H_2O where K_T is 450 10^{-6} MPa^{-1} for water and 125 10^{-6} MPa^{-1} for ice. We have returned to SAXS in order to characterise density fluctuations *in situ* at very high temperatures in $(Y_2O_3)_x$–$(Al_2O_3)_{1-x}$ melts. Previously studied by MacMillan and co-workers using rapidly quenched glasses [2], this system has attracted attention as an example of supercooled polyamorphism at ambient pressure, where phases of identical composition but of different density can coexist at a particular temperature. Measuring density *ex situ* in separated glasses the contrast between low and high density amorphous phases – LDA and HDA respectively – $\sqrt{\langle\Delta\rho^2\rangle}/\rho_0^2$ is ~ 0.04 [2].

RESULTS AND DISCUSSION

Laser-heated aerodynamic levitation techniques are required to reach the melting points of refractory liquids [3]. *In situ* SAXS from high temperature liquids was collected on station 6.2 at the Synchrotron Radiation Source Daresbury Laboratory, as described elsewhere at this conference [4].

Data for liquid and supercooled $Y_2Al_6O_{12}$ and $Y_2Al_8O_{15}$ are shown in Fig. 1, where a small rise in intensity with T can just be detected, shown by the arrows. SAXS is plotted as Log$I(Q)$ v Q^2 following convention [1]. A linear region can be identified shown by the dashed lines in Fig. 1 from which the expected increase in $I(0)$ with temperature can be obtained. There is however a sharp increase in $I(Q)$ as $Q \rightarrow 0$ beyond a minimum centred around 0.05Å^{-1} at the foot of the interatomic structure factor [5].

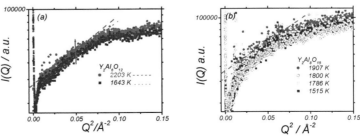

Figure 1. Temperature dependence of density fluctuations in $(Y_2O_3)_x$–$(Al_2O_3)_{1-x}$ melts recorded using SAXS: (a) $Y_2Al_6O_{12}$ and (b) $Y_2Al_8O_{15}$.

This can be seen more clearly in Fig. 2 where the same data are plotted as Log$I(Q)$ v Log$Q$. Whilst this prescription precludes determining $I(0)$, it reveals the power law rise in $I(Q)$ as $Q\rightarrow 0$. In addition, where for liquid $Y_2Al_6O_{12}$ SAXS increases with temperature throughout, as expected for widely dispersed thermal fluctuations (eq. 1), liquid $Y_2Al_8O_{15}$ is quite different at low Q, first increasing and then decreasing as the temperature rises towards the melting point. This is particularly striking at low Q indicating a transient zone of heterogeneity around 1800K distinct from thermal fluctuations. The zone is reversible and occurs over a very narrow temperature range, indicative of polyamorphism on the nanoscale [3,5].

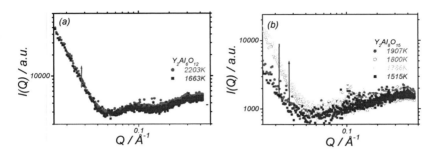

Figure 2. Log $I(Q)$ v Log Q data for liquid and supercooled $Y_2Al_6O_{12}$ (a) and $Y_2Al_8O_{15}$ (b).

The two linear regions of the log$I(Q)$ versus log$Q$ plots in Fig. 2 suggest a simple procedure for removing the structure factor contribution at high Q that appears to underlie the low Q regime. Using the power law relations evident in Fig. 2, the low Q limb (Q<0.04Å^{-1}) has been normalised in Fig. 3 by extrapolating the high Q limb into the same Q range.

A very interesting outcome in the resulting SAXS profile is a form factor minimum centred around 0.05Å^{-1} which is illustrated for liquid $Y_2Al_6O_{12}$. Fitting the reduced SAXS using the from factor expression for spherical particles

$$I(Q) = C\left[3\frac{\sin QR - QR\cos QR}{(QR)^3}\right]^2$$ yields a mean radius R close to 120Å with the asymmetric size distribution shown in Fig 3(b). The mean volume of such fluctuating elements illustrated in Fig. 3(b) is around ~6.5 10^6 Å^3 which is considerably larger than for thermal fluctuations [1]. This suggests that longer range fluctuations are present in these fragile $(Y_2O_3)_x$–$(Al_2O_3)_{1-x}$ liquids in addition to those that derive simply from compressibility.

Returning to Fig. 2(b) the enhanced SAXS close to 1800K for supercooled $Y_2Al_8O_{15}$ compared to the thermal background is ~4, so calibrating the SAXS peak to $\sqrt{\langle\Delta\rho^2\rangle}/\rho_0^2 \sim 0.04$ gives a thermal background of ~0.02 [5]. The compressibility of $Y_2Al_6O_{12}$ glass at RT is 9 10^{-6} MPa^{-1} [6]. If we assume that above the melting point this triples to 27 10^{-6} MPa^{-1} in line with silica, then eq. 1 indicates that the volume of thermal fluctuations in liquid $Y_2Al_6O_{12}$ is ~2 10^3 Å^3. This is smaller than the volume V of density fluctuations for silica at T_g [1] and minute compared to the large fluctuations inferred from Fig. 3. Long range fluctuations with correlation lengths far larger than the scale of thermal fluctuations have been reported in fragile organic liquids [7], where they appear to be linked to the dynamic heterogeneity [8] observed close to the critical temperature predicted by Mode Coupling Theory.

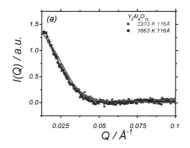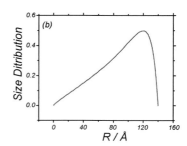

Figure 3. (a) Reduced Log $I(Q)$vQ SAXS profile for liquid and supercooled $Y_2Al_6O_{12}$. Form factor fitting is shown by the solid curve for the bimodal particle distribution shown in (b).

ACKNOWLEDGMENTS

We would like to thank the Higher Education Funding Council of Wales for support through the Centre for Advanced Functional Materials and Devices and the Science and Technology Facilities Council for providing access to the SRS.

REFERENCES

1. J. Zarzycki, *Glasses and the Vitreous State*, Cambridge: Cambridge University Press, 1991.
2. S. Aasland and P.F. McMillan, *Nature* **369**, , 633. (1994)
3. P.F. McMillan et al *J. Phys.: Condens. Matter* **19**, 415101 (2007)
4. M.C. Wilding et al– SRMS-6.
5. G.N. Greaves, M.C. Wilding, S. Fearn, D. Langstaff, F. Kargl, S. Cox, O. Majérus, Q. Vu Van, C.J. Benmore, R. Weber, C.M. Martin and L. Hennet, *Science* **322**, 566 (2008).
6. A. Yeganeh-Haeri et al, *Journal of Non- Crystalline Solids* **241**, 200 (1998)
7. A. Patkowski et al, *Phys. Rev E*, **61**, 6909 (2000)
8. N. Greaves and A. Angell, *Current Opinion in Solid State & Materials Science* **3**, 361 (1998),

Ca Dopant in BaTiO$_3$ by X-ray Absorption Near-Edge Structure

Toshihiro Okajima[a,b], Katsumasa Yasukawa[c]

[a]Kyushu Synchrotron Light Research Center, okajima@saga-ls.jp, 8-7 Yayoigaoka, Tosu, Saga 841-0005, Japan
[b]Faculty of Engineering, Kyushu Univ., 744 motooka, nishi-ku, Fukuoka 819-0395, Japan
[c]R&D Center, Kyocera Corp., 1-4 Kokubuyamashitao, Kirishima, Kagoshima 899-4312, Japan

Abstract. The local structure of Ca dopant in BaTiO$_3$ is investigated by Ca K-edge X-ray absorption fine structure (XANES) spectroscopy. In conjunction with the experiments, first-principles calculations are systematically made. Projector augmented wave method is made to optimize the local structure. Augmented plane wave plus local orbitals method is adopted to obtain theoretical XANES spectrum. A comparison between experimental and XANES spectra shows Ca dopants are located at the Ba site.

Keywords: first-principles calculations, X-ray absorption near-edge structure spectroscopy, dopant, barium taitanate
PACS(s): 61.05.cj, 77.84.-s

INTRODUCTION

BaTiO$_3$ (BTO) is a typical ferroelectric material with the perovskite-type crystal structure. The BTO shows very high dielectric constant in the vicinity of room temperature. Multi-Layer Ceramic Capacitor (MLCC) using the BTO with dopant, such as Ca, Mg and Sr, contributes to miniaturizing and making to high performance of portable equipment. However, because it is a difficulty of the experiment, the state of solid solutions of the dopant has not been well understood. In the present study, we investigate the local structure of Ca dopant in BTO by the combination of XANES spectroscopy and first-principles calculations.

EXPERIMENTAL AND COMPUTATIONAL PROCEDURE

Sample of Ca doped BaTiO$_3$ (BaTiO$_3$:Ca) powders were purchased by SAKAI Chemical Industry Co., Ltd (Osaka, JAPAN). The concentration of Ca was 5 atomic percentages. High-purity CaTiO$_3$ powder was used as a reference sample. XANES spectra measurement of BaTiO$_3$:Ca and CaTiO$_3$ at Ca K-edge were performed at BL15 at SAGA Light Source [1].

CP1092, *Synchrotron Radiation in Materials Science: 6th International Conference*, edited by R. Magalhaes-Paniago
© 2009 American Institute of Physics 978-0-7354-0625-4/09/$25.00

Prior to the calculations for XANES spectra, the structural optimizations were performed using the PAW method, as implemented in the VASP code [2]. In the calculations, $2\times2\times2$ supercells (40 atoms) were employed. Four types of models were examined by changing the positions of Ca dopants and oxygen vacancy. Model BCTO contains a substitutional Ca atom at Ba site. Model BTCO_V1 contains a substitutional Ca atom at Ti site. Models BTCO_V2 and V3 contain a substitutional Ca atoms at Ti sites and one V_O. Here the V_O is introduced to compensate the charge imbalance due to a Ca^{2+} ion instead of a Ti^{4+} ion. In each model of BTCO_V2 and BTCO_V3, the V_O was located at the first nearest-neighboring (NN) position from Ca atom. The difference was that the V_O was located in the a-b plane of BTCO_V2 and the V_O was located along the c axis for model BTCO_V3. Theoretical Ca K-edge XANES spectra for the $BaTiO_3$:Ca and $CaTiO_3$ were obtained using the FLAPW + lo package, WIEN2k [3]. The core-hole effects were fully taken into account in the present calculations.

RESULTS AND DISCUSSION

The experimental Ca K-edge XANES spectrum is shown in FIGURE 1 together with the theoretical spectra calculated for four typed of models. The experimental XANES spectrum of $BaTiO_3$:Ca can be reproduced by model BCTO. It is also interesting that a clear chemical shift can be seen depending upon the choice of the model. Models BTCO_V1, V2, and V3 show the peak top energies of these models are shifted more than that of model BCTO. The strong pre-edge peak at around 4037 eV for models BTCO_V2 and V3 are not appeared in experimental one. These disagreements can be ascribed to the wrong assumption of the model a substitutional Ca atom at Ti site. The experimental spectrum clearly indicates the model a substitutional Ca atom at Ba site.

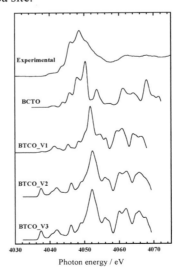

FIGURE 1. Comparison of experimental and theoretical Ca K-edge XANES spectra of Ca dopans in $BaTiO_3$.

TABLE 1. Local structures of Ca atom in model BCTO and Ba atom in model BTO.

model	bond	atomic distance / Å	CNs*
BCTO	Ca-O	2.564	4
		2.780	4
		3.055	4
BTO	Ba-O	2.814	4
		2.829	4
		2.891	4

*CNs : coordination numbers

The local structures of Ca atom for atomic distance and coordination numbers for NN atoms in Model BCTO are summarized in TABLE 1. The coordination numbers of O around Ba are in model BTO, and the atomic distance are 12 and almost 2.85 Å, respectively. These results are as same as the values obtained from experimental result. On the other hand, the atomic distances O and substitutional Ca atom at Ba site in model BCTO are not the same as those of Ba-O in BTO. We can see that the atomic position of Ca atom in model BCTO shifts to one direction from this table. FIGURE 2 shows the optimized structure by projector augmented wave method for model BCTO together with BTO. The small red sphere, small blue sphere, large green, and large blue sphere denote O atoms, Ti atoms, Ba atoms, and Ca atoms, respectively. We can see that the Ca atoms in model BCTO shift to the direction of c-axis by inspection of FIGURE 2. It is considered that the displacement of Ca atom along c-axis is concerned with the improvement of the dielectric properties on $BaTiO_3$.

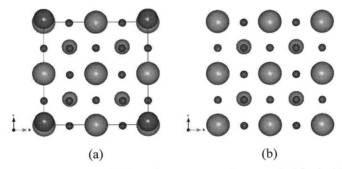

(a)   (b)

FIGURE 2. Optimized structures by the Projector augmented wave method for the (a) Ca doped $BaTiO_3$ and (b) $BaTiO_3$.

CONCLUSIONS

In this study, the local environment of Ca dopant in $BaTiO_3$ has been examined by the combination of Ca K-edge XANES measurements and first-principles density function theory (DFT) calculations. XANES spectra of Ca doped $BaTiO_3$ were observed at beamline 15 of SAGA-LS using fluorescence mode. The observed XANES spectrum of Ca doped $BaTiO_3$ at Ca K-edge was represented the calculated spectrum using the structure model substituted from Ba atom at A site in $BaTiO_3$ to Ca atom. Furthermore, the Ca atoms shift to the direction to c-axis. The present study clearly demonstrated that the combination of XANES measurements and first-principles DFT calculations is a powerful method of identifying the local structures of dopant in $BaTiO_3$.

ACKNOWLEDGMENTS

This work was performed under the approval of the SAGS-LS Advisory Committee (proposal nos. 070728G and 070616G). One of authors (T.O.) was supported by a research granted from The Murata Science Foundation.

REFERENCES

1. T. Okajima, Y. Chikaura, Y. Suzuki, M. Tabata, Y. Soejima, K. Hara, R. Haruki, K. Nagata, N. Hiramatsu, A. Khono, M. Takumi, H. Setoyama, D. Yoshimura, " The Design and Performance of Beamline BL15 at SAGA Light Source" in *Synchrotron Radiation Instrumentation: Ninth International Conference*, edited by J-Y. Choi and S. Rah, AIP Conf. Proc. 879, American Institute of Physics, Melville, NY, 2007, pp. 820-823.
2. G. Kresse, J. Hafner: *Phys. Rev. B* **47**, 558 (1993).
3. P. Blaha, *et. al.*, *WIEN2k, An Aurgmented Plane Wave + Local Orbital Program for Calculating Crystal Properties*, K. Schwarz, Ed.; Techn. Universitat Wien, Austria, 2001.

In-situ X-ray structure measurements on aerodynamically levitated high temperature liquids.

Richard Weber*[1,2], Christopher Benmore[2], Qiang Mei[2] and Martin Wilding[3]

1. *Materials Development, Inc., Arlington Hts., IL 60004, USA, rweber@matsdev.com*
2. *Argonne National Laboratory, benmore@anl.gov, qiang.mei@hpcat.aps.anl.gov,*
3. *University of Wales, mbw@aber.edu*

Abstract. High energy, high flux X-ray sources enable new measurements of liquid and amorphous materials in extreme conditions. Aerodynamic levitation in combination with laser beam heating can be used to access high purity and non-equilibrium liquids at temperatures up to 3000 K. In this work, a small aerodynamic levitator was integrated with high energy beamline 11 ID-C at the Advanced Photon Source. Scattered X-rays were detected with a Mar345 image plate. The experiments investigated a series of binary in the $CaO-Al_2O_3$, $MgO-SiO_2$, $SiO_2-Al_2O_3$ metal oxide compositions and pure SiO_2. The results show that the liquids exhibit large changes in structure when the predominant network former is diluted. Measurements on glasses with the same compositions as the liquids suggest that significant structural rearrangement consistent with a fragile-strong transition occurs in these reluctant glass forming liquids as they vitrify.

Keywords: Materials Science, Synchrotron radiation
PACS: 81.00.00

INTRODUCTION

Extreme sample environments provide unique opportunities when they are used in combination with high flux x-ray sources. The use of aerodynamic levitation with laser beam heating provides a convenient way to access very high temperature liquids in conditions that avoid contamination and heterogeneous nucleation by container walls [1,2]. This enables (i) the study of metastable high temperature liquids, and (ii) formation of new glasses. The aerodynamic levitation technique is extremely versatile and compact and it has been used to study liquid metals, oxides and integrated with NMR, neutron, and x-ray facilities [3,4].

The present research is focused on investigation of fragile binary oxide liquids. These liquids exhibit a highly non-Arrhenius temperature dependence of viscosity [5]. In many cases fragile liquids can be vitrified using levitation methods. The study of

CP1092, *Synchrotron Radiation in Materials Science: 6th International Conference*, edited by R. Magalhaes-Paniago
© 2009 American Institute of Physics 978-0-7354-0625-4/09/$25.00

the high temperature liquid and the corresponding glass structure provides insights in structural evolution as the liquid cools, its viscosity increases, and ultimately the glass transition occurs.

EXPERIMENTAL METHODS

A photograph of the laboratory-based aerodynamic levitation facility at the Advanced Photon Source is shown in Fig. 1. This instrument is used in the laboratory to synthesize glasses and investigate undercooling of liquids. The instrument can be installed at the high energy beamline 11 ID-C for *in-situ* measurements on liquids. The sample temperature is measured using an optical pyrometer and progress of the experiments is followed from outside the beamline hutch using video cameras that view the sample. Samples approximately 3 mm in diameter can be levitated in process gases (oxygen or argon, which is necessary for metals).

In the x-ray experiments, scattered x-rays are detected using a Mar-345 image plate that is located approximately 50 cm from the sample. The x-ray beam is 1 x 1 mm and intersects the top part of the sample in the region where it is heated and where the temperature is measured. The instrument is calibrated using a standard CeO_2 sample and then the materials to be investigated are introduced into the levitator.

Figure 1. Image of the aerodynamic levitation facility at the Advanced Photon Source. Binary oxide compositions are made by fusing high purity metal oxide powder mixtures.

A schematic layout of the experimental set up is illustrated in Fig. 2. A tungsten pin loc ated at the center of the image plate blocks the direct x-ray beam. Scattered x-ray data is acquired by computer and analyzed using procedures established in prior work [6].

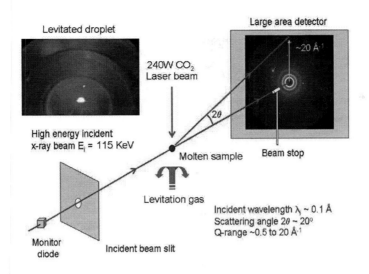

Figure 2 - Illustration of the experimental set up at the beamline. By using an incident x-ray energy of 115 keV a Q-range of *ca.* 20Å^{-1} is obtained

Silica. High purity silica glass and the corresponding liquid were investigated at temperatures from 25-2100°C [6]. The strong liquid exhibits very minor structure changes with temperature: (i) ~2% increase in Si-O bond length from 25 to 1600°C, and (ii) the average bond angle decreases ~9° at high temperature, indicating small changes in polymer ring size

CaO-Al$_2$O$_3$ binaries. The materials melt to form fragile liquids that can be vitrified over a range from approximately 50-70 mole % CaO. The derived D(r) for liquids at 2000°C and glass at ambient temperature are presented in Fig. 3.

While the Al-O first nearest neighbor distance is essentially the same in the glass and liquid, there are significant changes in the Ca-O bonding and the correlations at longer distances. NMR measurements on similar glasses indicated that AlO$_4$ triclusters are present in compositions containing 50% CaO but not in those with higher CaO contents [8,9]. MD simulations on the liquid [10] indicate a substantial concentration of triclusters in the liquid.

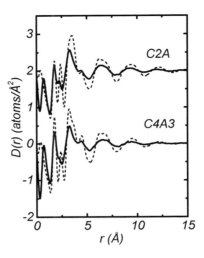

Figure 3. Comparison of the structures of liquid and glass for two compositions in the CaO-Al$_2$O$_3$ binary system shown out to long distances, glass is the dashed line – see ref [7].

MgO-SiO$_2$ binaries. Detailed structure measurements across the MgSiO$_3$-Mg$_2$SiO$_4$ region show that there is a transition from predominantly SiO$_2$ network to MgO network at approximately 38 mole % SiO$_2$ in the glass. Measurements on the corresponding high temperature liquids suggest that the transition in network behavior occurs at approximately 48 mole % SiO$_2$ in the liquid.

Al$_2$O$_3$-SiO$_2$ binaries. Measurements were made on liquids containing 30-90 mole% Al$_2$O$_3$. The melt structure is remarkably constant over this range comprising predominantly 4-coordinated Si-O and Al-O species. Simulations indicate a high population of AlO$_4$ triclusters in the liquids. In contrast, glasses formed in this system show high populations of 5 and 6-coordinated aluminum ions [11].

DISCUSSION

For the three binary oxide systems investigated, there are substantial differences in structure between the glass at ambient temperature and the high temperature liquid. In the case of the aluminates, the presence of triclusters of AlO$_4$ species appears to be common in the high temperature liquids. On cooling, the concentration of triclusters decreases and the glasses frequently contain higher coordinated aluminum species. In the magnesium silicates, changes in Mg-O bonding occur as the liquid is cooled.

The high and low temperature structural 'snapshots" enabled by the high energy x-ray experiments provide a new insight into the structural evolution of the liquids with temperature. Ongoing research is targeted towards understanding the temperature dependence of structure as the liquids approach the glass transition. One key goal of this work is to determine if the fragile-strong transition exhibits the character of a phase transition or a slow evolution of structure with changing temperature.

ACKNOWLEDGMENTS

This work was supported by the U.S. DOE, at Argonne National Laboratory under contract number DE-AC02-06CH11357.

REFERENCES

1. S. Ansell. S. Krishnan, J.K.R. Weber, J.J. Felten, P.C. Nordine, M.A. Beno, D.L. Price and M-L Saboungi, *Phys. Rev. Lett.*, 1997, 78, 464.
2. J. J. Wall, R. Weber, J. Kim, P. K. Liaw, and H. Choo, *Mater. Sci. Eng. A*, 2007, 445-446, 219.
3. C. Landron, L. Hennet, J.-P. Coutures, T.E. Jenkins, C. Aletru, G.N. Greaves, A.K. Soper and G. Derbyshire, *Rev. Sci. Instrum.*, 2000, 71, 1745.
4. J.K.R. Weber, C.J. Benmore, J.A. Tangeman, J. Siewenie and K.J. Hiera, *J. Neutron Res.*, 2003, 11, 113.
5. F. H. Stillinger, *Science,* 1995, 267, 1935..
6. Q. Mei, C.J. Benmore and J.K.R. Weber, *Phys. Rev. Lett,* 2007, 98, 057802.
7. Q. Mei, C.J. Benmore, J. Kim, J.K.R. Weber, J.E. Rix and M.C. Wilding, *J. Phys. Cond. Matt.*, in press.
8. D. Iuga, C. Morais, Z. Gan, D.R. Neuville, L. Cormier, and D. Massiot,, *J. Am. Chem. Soc.* 2005, 127, 11540.
9. J.R. Allwardt, S.K. Lee and J.F. Stebbins, *Am. Miner.*, 2003, 88, 949.
10. S. Kohara, Spring-8, private communication.
11. S. Sen, R.E. Youngman. *J. Phys. Chem. B,* 2004 108, 7557.

Temperature Scanning SAXD/ WAXD Measurements On Stratum Corneum Of Mammalian Skin To Separate Entangled Structures

Ichiro Hatta, Noboru Ohta and Naoto Yagi

Japan Synchrotron Radiation Research Institute, SPring-8, 1-1-1 Kouto, Sayo, Hyogo 679-5198, Japan

Abstract. The outermost layer of skin, the stratum corneum (SC), is composed of corneocytes and an intercellular lipid matrix. The matrix acts as the main barrier. In the SC, the longitudinal arrangement of the lipid molecules consists of long and short lamellar structures and the lateral arrangement consists of hexagonal and orthorhombic hydrocarbon-chain packings. From the temperature dependence of SAXD/WAXD, we revealed that a long lamellar structure is formed by hexagonal hydrocarbon-chain packing and a short lamellar structure by orthorhombic hydrocarbon-chain packing.

Keywords: lipid, lamellar structure, hydrocarbon chain, phase transition.
PACS: 87.15.bk

INTRODUCTION

The intercellular lipid matrix of the stratum corneum (SC) plays an important role in transepidermal drug delivery, barrier functions, etc. [1, 2], where the stratum corneum is expressed by so-called a brick-mortar model as shown in Fig. 1. To elucidate these molecular mechanisms, an understanding of the structure of the intercellular lipid matrix is essential. The structure in the SC is characterized in terms of two orthogonal lattice spacings: one is due to the longitudinal lamellar repeat distance and the other to the lattice constant of the transverse hydrocarbon-chain packing. In SAXD studies of various mammalian SCs, a long lamellar structure with a repeat distance of about 13 nm has been predominantly observed (see Fig. 2 (a)), together with a less distinct short lamellar structure with a repeat distance of about 6 nm (see Fig. 2 (b)) [3]. It should be stressed that under hydrated conditions with heavy water, only the short lamellar structure has clearly been observed by neutron diffraction (ND) [4]. This observation is explained by the uneven distribution of water in the two structures: the long lamellar structure does not contain water and hence contributes weakly to ND, whereas the short lamellar structure contributes predominantly to ND [4]. As for the transverse hydrocarbon-chain packings, hexagonal hydrocarbon-chain packing with a lattice constant of 0.42 nm and

CP1092, *Synchrotron Radiation in Materials Science: 6th International Conference*, edited by R. Magalhaes-Paniago
© 2009 American Institute of Physics 978-0-7354-0625-4/09/$25.00

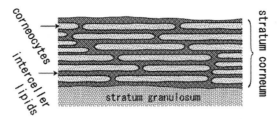

FIGURE 1. A brick-and-mortar model for stratum corneum (SC). Corneocytes are embedded in the intercellular lipid matrix of the SC.

(a)   (b)

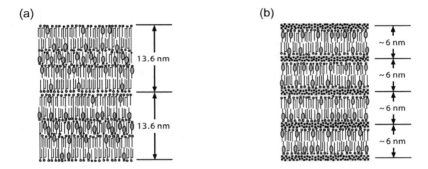

FIGURE 2. (a) The long lamellar structure, and (b) the short lamellar structure in the intercellular lipid matrix of the SC. The lamellar structures are composed of a variety of lipids, such as ceramides, fatty acids, and cholesterol. In the short lamellar structure, there is a water layer between the lipid layers.

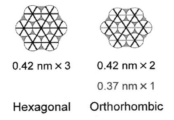

0.42 nm × 3   0.42 nm × 2
                     0.37 nm × 1

Hexagonal   Orthorhombic

FIGURE 3. The hexagonal and the orthorhombic hydrocarbon-chain packings in the cross section normal to the long axis of the lipid molecules in the intercellular lipid matrix of the SC.

hexagonal hydrocarbon-chain packing with a lattice constant of 0.42 nm and orthorhombic packing with lattice constants of 0.42 nm and 0.37 nm have been observed by WAXD for various mammalian SCs (see Fig. 3) [5]. Because the lattice constant of 0.42 nm is coincidentally common to both the hexagonal and the orthorhombic hydrocarbon-chain packings, superimposition of the diffraction peaks on WAXD makes detailed data analysis difficult. Based upon the dependence of SAXD/WAXD on temperature we aim to make clear the correspondence between the longitudinal lamellar structures (long or short) and the transverse packing (hexagonal or orthorhombic).

MATERIALS AND METHODS

Hairless mice (HR-1, Hoshino, Japan) were used. The SC was separated from the skin. We used SC samples with the hydration of about 25 wt%.

The differential scanning calorimetry (DSC) measurement was performed in the temperature range of 5-120° C using a DSC apparatus (Q1000, TA Instruments, DE, USA) [6]. The DSC cell was purged with dry nitrogen at 50 cm^3/min. A scanning rate was 10° C/min. The sample mass was 10 mg. The sample was hermetically sealed into a 7.5 μl aluminum pan.

The SAXD/WAXD experiments were performed at BL40B2 (Structural Biology II Beamline) of SPring-8 (Hyogo, Japan). X-ray diffraction profiles were recorded using an imaging plate system (R-AXIS IV; Rigaku, Tokyo, Japan) with a 30×30 cm^2 area. The X-ray wavelength was 0.083 nm and the sample-to-detector distance was about 400 mm. The reciprocal spacing $S = (2/\lambda)\sin\theta$ was calibrated by using the lattice spacing ($d = 5.838$ nm; d is the lamellar repeat distance) of a silver behenate crystal at room temperature, where 2θ is the scattering angle. The exposure time was 30 s. The diffraction pattern was circularly averaged to obtain a radial intensity profile. The temperature of the sample was controlled using a temperature regulator (SR-50; Shimaden Co., Tokyo, Japan), and was measured with a thermocouple embedded in the sample holder. All the experiments were performed in the first heating scan at a rate of 0.5 K min^{-1}. Because the radiation damage was only small, we assumed that this effect was not serious in the analysis of the results.

RESULTS

Figure 4 shows the endothermic and the exothermic curves for the hairless mouse SC. As seen in Fig. 4, in the first heating run the endothermic peaks take place at ①33° C, ②39° C, ③52° C, ④73° C, ⑤97° C and in the second heating run a broad single endothermic peak appears near 56° C. In the first and the second cooling run exothermic peaks take place at 37° C and at 48° C. It is worth to point out that only in the first heating run we can observe two successive peaks not only at 33° but also at 39° C. To confirm the reproducibility of these endothermic peaks the DSC measurement was performed in the other hairless mouse SC. These endothermic peaks take place almost in the same manner as in Fig. 4. Therefore, the reproducibility is satisfactory.

To resolve the correlation between the lamellar structure and the lateral packing, we carried out temperature scanning SAXD and WAXD measurements on the hairless mouse SC with especial attention to the phase transitions observed by the DSC. The SAXD and WAXD data from the SCs are plotted against temperature in Fig. 5(a) and (b) [7]. From the highly sensitive differential scanning calorimetry (DSC) [6], the transition temperatures of the intercellular lipid matrix in the hairless mouse SC are indicated by thick horizontal lines in Fig. 5(a) and (b). A thin horizontal line is drawn in Fig. 5(a) and (b) at about 56 °C, where a broad maximum was observed by the DSC.

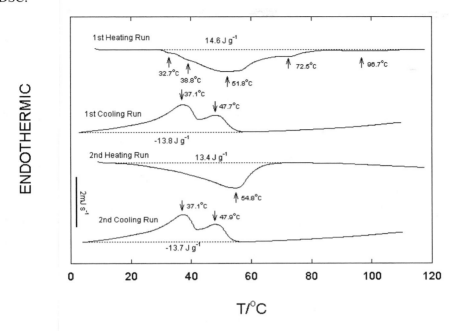

FIGURE 4. The endothermic and the exothermic DSC curves of the hairless mouse stratum corneum. The curves for the first heating, the first cooling, the second heating, and the second cooling runs are shown from the top to the bottom, successively.

The thick line observed near 100 °C by the DSC indicates an anomaly associated with proteins [6]. The intensity contours for both SAXD and WAXD were essentially the same in all the samples measured. By comparing the results from SAXD and WAXD, we found that both the thick curve B and the thick curve D occur in the same temperature range, from 52 °C to 73 °C. It should be noted that the thick curve B is the trace of the diffraction peak for the short lamellar structure; the thick curve D is the trace of the diffraction peak for the high-temperature hexagonal hydrocarbon-chain packing originating from the orthorhombic hydrocarbon-chain packing at room temperature; however, the counterpart of the thick curve A corresponds to the dotted curve C, because they appear in the same temperature range, from 33 °C to 56 °C. The thick curve A is the trace of the diffraction peak for the long lamellar structure; and the dotted curve C seems to be the trace of the diffraction peak for the liquid-crystalline-like hydrocarbon-chain packing originating from the low-temperature hexagonal hydrocarbon-chain packing. It should be pointed out that the origin of the low-temperature hydrocarbon-chain packing is completely different from that of high-temperature one, since the lattice constant in higher temperature becomes generally larger but the lattice constant of the low-temperature hexagonal hydrocarbon-chain packing is larger than that of high temperature one. As a result owing to the transition from the low-temperature hexagonal to the liquid-crystalline-like hydrocarbon-chain, the intensity contours bend at 33°C and finally merge into those of the liquid-crystalline hydrocarbon-chain packing near 90°C. Therefore, we propose the

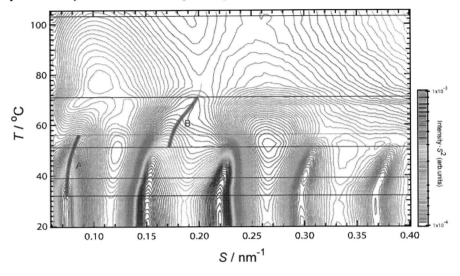

Figure 5. (a) Temperature dependence of the intensity contours of SAXD. The diffraction peaks of the long lamellar structure take place from the 1st to the 5th order. The trace of the 1st order peak is denoted by A. The diffraction peak of the short lamellar structure denoted by B was observed only between 52 and 73°C.

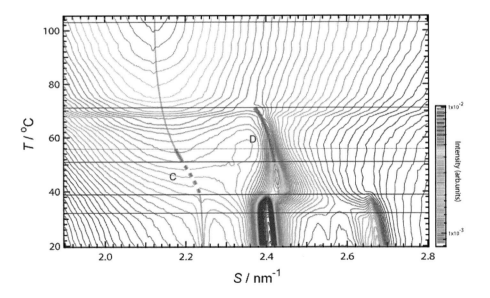

Figure 5. (b) Temperature dependence of the intensity contours of SAXD. The diffraction peaks of orthorhombic hydrocarbon-chain packing takes place and disappears at 39°C. Above 39°C only the higher temperature hexagonal hydrocarbon -chain packing takes place.

coexistence of two domains at room temperature in the SC: one composed of the long lamellar structure with the low-temperature hexagonal hydrocarbon-chain packing, and the other composed of the short lamellar structure with the orthorhombic hydrocarbon-chain packing [7].

DISCUSSION

In order to verify the above proposal quantitatively, we will perform an analysis in terms of the shape factor in a self-organized lipid assembly, as suggested by Israelachvili [8]. Generally, the fluid-like hydrocarbon chain is taken into account when considering a variety of the structures of a self-organized lipid assembly. Temperature rises increase the disorder of a hydrocarbon chain, involving *trans–gauche* isomerization, and thereby reduce the limiting length of a hydrocarbon chain. On the other hand, the head-group area depends on the nature of the lipid [9]. At a temperature the whole structure of a self-organized lipid assembly is formed so as to be compatible with the state of the disordered hydrocarbon chain and the head-group

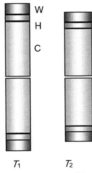

T_1 T_2

Figure 6. A pair of lipid molecules at two temperatures ($T_1 < T_2$). A molecule is composed of hydrocarbon chain and head-group and a water layer faces hydrophilic head-group.

area. At present we only confine our interest to a lamellar structure which appears in the intercellular lipid matrix of the SC. In the above consideration the thickness of a head-group has not been taken into account. We modify the shape factor for the analysis of the structure formed by a self-organized lipid assembly in the intercellular lipid matrix of the SC. We consider the contribution of not only the thickness of a hydrocarbon chain but also those of a head-group and a water layer. In fact, from the analysis of SAXD in the lamellar structure of a phospholipid assembly the electron density distribution is composed of the thicknesses of the hydrocarbon chain, the head-group and the water layer [10]. Then, we modify the concept of the shape factor by adding the thicknesses of a head-group and a water layer. In Fig. 6, a pair of lipid molecules with water layers is shown schematically at temperatures T_1 and T_2 ($T_1 < T_2$), where the hydrocarbon chain, the head-group and the water layer are denoted by **C**, **H** and **W**, respectively. The total length from the top of the water layer and the bottom of the water layer corresponds to the lamellar repeat distance. When temperature changes, the structure composed of a pair of lipid molecules alters due to the cooperated interaction of the shape of disordered hydrocarbon chain and head-group area with keeping a lamellar structure, in addition the thickness of the water layer follows the above change of the head-group area. Then, we define a modified shape factor as

$$\frac{v}{a_0 l_c},\tag{1}$$

where a_0 is the cross-sectional area of a rod-like hydrocarbon chain, l_c is the lamellar repeat distance, and v is the effective volume occupied by a hydrocarbon chain, a part of a lipid head-group, and a water layer. For a lamellar structure, the modified shape factor is equal to unity, that is,

$$\frac{v}{a_0 l_c} = 1, \ \text{i.e.,} \ \ v = a_0 l_c.\tag{2}$$

When temperature increases, the hydrocarbon chain becomes disorder, i.e., the hydrocarbon-chain packing becomes loose and the lamellar repeat distance becomes short: When l_c becomes small, a_0 becomes large. As a result, we can expect that the effective volume v is almost constant and then, $a_0 l_c$ is unchanged in a short temperature interval in a single phase (note Eq. 2). Namely, as seen in Fig. 6 when temperature rises from T_1 to T_2 the lamellar repeat distance decreases and the head-

Table 1. Analysis based upon the modified shape factor for the short lamellar structure in the intercellular lipid matrix of the SC. The cross-sectional area, a_0, obtained from the lattice constant of the high-temperature hexagonal hydrocarbon-chain packing, the lamellar repeat distance, l_c and the calculated volume, $a_0 l_c$.

Temperature (℃)	a_0 (nm^2)	l_c (nm)	$a_0 l_c$ (nm^3)
50	0.197	5.95	1.17
55	0.198	5.81	1.15
60	0.199	5.75	1.14
65	0.201	5.46	1.10

Table 2. Analysis based upon the modified shape factor for the long lamellar structure in the intercellular lipid matrix of the SC. The cross-sectional area, a_0, obtained from the lattice constant of the liquid-crystalline-like structure, the lamellar repeat distance, l_c and the calculated volume, $a_0 l_c$.

Temperature (℃)	a_0 (nm^2)	l_c (nm)	$a_0 l_c$ (nm^3)
35.0	0.229	13.37	3.062
52.5	0.238	12.88	3.065

| 55.0 | 0.239 | 12.64 | 3.026 |

group area increases with keeping the total volume nearly constant.

First, we apply the modified shape factor to the quantitative analysis of the relation between the thick curve B and the thick curve D for the short lamellar structure in Fig. 5 (a) an (b), respectively. From the curve B we can obtain the lamellar repeat distance l_c and from the curve D the head-group area a_0. The analyzed a_0 and l_c together with the calculated volume $a_0 l_c$ are listed in Table 1 at temperatures, 50, 55, 60, and 65°C. As seen in Table 1, in the above temperature interval $a_0 l_c$ is almost constant. Therefore, the fact that in the short lamellar structure the curve B is related to the curve D can be confirmed satisfactorily. Second, we further carry out the quantitative analysis of the relation between the thick curve A and the thick curve C for the long lamellar structure in Fig. 5 (a) and (b), respectively. Although in the long lamellar structure there is no water layer and a lipid layer is composed of a tri-lamellar structure as shown in Fig. 2 (a), we can apply the modified shape factor also to the analysis of the long lamellar structure. The curve A clearly indicates the trace of the 1st order diffraction of the long lamellar structure. The counterpart of the thick curve A corresponds to the dotted curve C, because they appear in the same temperature range, from 33 °C to 56 °C. The dotted curve C seems to be the trace of the diffraction peak for the liquid-crystalline-like hydrocarbon-chain packing originating from the low-temperature hexagonal hydrocarbon-chain packing. On the basis of high-resolution DSC [6], it has been proposed that at 33°C the phase transition from the low-temperature hexagonal to the liquid-crystalline-like state takes place. The broad liquid–crystalline-like ridge observed near 33°C seems to finally turn into a broad peak near 0.46 nm (S = 2.18 nm^{-1}) for a liquid–crystalline phase above 56°C. Then, we predict that the trace of the diffraction peak for the liquid-crystalline-like hydrocarbon-chain packing is given by the dotted curve C connected smoothly between 2.245 nm^{-1} near 33°C and 2.20 nm^{-1} near 56°C, where below 33°C the precursor of the diffraction peak at 2.245 nm^{-1} appears as seen in Fig. 5 (b) (in detail see Ref. 7). From the curve A we can obtain the long lamellar repeat distance l_c and from the curve C the head-group area a_0. The analyzed a_0 and l_c together with the calculated volume $a_0 l_c$ are listed in Table 2 at temperatures, 35.0, 52.5, and 55.0°C. As seen in Table 2, in the above temperature interval $a_0 l_c$ is almost constant. the dotted curve and as a result, the long lamellar structure is formed by the hexagonal hydrocarbon-chain packing.

CONCLUSIONS

Based upon the result of the temperature dependence of SAXD/WAXD of the intercellular lipid matrix in the hairless mouse stratum corneum, we propose that there are two domains in the intercellular lipid matrix; one is the long lamellar structure with hexagonal hydrocarbon-chain packing and the other the short lamellar structure with orthorhombic packing. As pointed out in our previous paper [11], the long lamellar structure has hydrophobic nature and on the other hand the short lamellar structure has hydrophilic nature. Then, based upon these structural evidence we can thoroughly elucidate the mechanisms of cosmetic function, percutaneous transport, etc.

REFERENCES

[1] P. M. Elias and G. K. Menon, *Adv. Lipid Res.* **24**, 1–26 (1991).

[2] B. W. Barry, *Adv. Drug Deliv. Rev.* **54** Suppl. 1, S31–S40 (2002).

[3] J. A. Bouwstra, P. L. Honeywell-Nguyen, G. S. Gooris, and M. Ponec, *Progr. Lipid Res.* **42**, 1–36 (2003).

[4] G. C. Charalambopoulou, T. A. Steriotis, T. Hauss, A. K. Stubos, and N. K. Kanelloupoulos, *Physica* B **350**, e603–e606 (2004).

[5] J. A. Bouwstra, G. S. Gooris, M. A. Salomons-de Vries, J. A. van der Spek, and W. Bras, *Int. J. Pharm.* **84**, 205–216 (1992).

[6] I. Hatta, K. Nakanishi, and K. Ishikiriyama, *Thermochim. Acta* **431**, 94–97 (2005).

[7] I. Hatta, N. Ohta, K. Inoue and N. Yagi, *Biochim. Biophys. Acta* **1758**, 1830-1836 (2006).

[8] J. N. Israelachvili, *Intermolecular & Surface Forces* 2nd Ed. (Academic Press, London, 1992) p. 371.

[9] J. N. Israelachvili, *Intermolecular & Surface Forces* 2nd Ed. (Academic Press, London, 1992) p. 380.

[10]J. F. Nagle and S. Tristram-Nagle, *Biochim. Biophys. Acta* **1469**, 159-195 (2000).

[11]N. Ohta, S. Ban, H. Tanaka, S. Nakata, and I. Hatta, *Chem. Phys. Lipids* **123**, 1–8 (2003).

An Efficient Referencing And Sample Positioning System To Investigate Heterogeneous Substances With Combined Microfocused Synchrotron X-ray Techniques

Thomas Spangenberg[a], Jörg Göttlicher[a], Ralph Steininger[a]

[a]Forschungszentrum Karlsruhe GmbH, Institute for Synchrotron Radiation,
Synchrotron Radiation Source ANKA, Hermann-von-Helmholtz-Platz 1,
76344 Eggenstein-Leopoldshafen, Germany

Abstract. A referencing and sample positioning system has been developed to transfer object positions measured with an offline microscope to a synchrotron experimental station. The accuracy should be sufficient to deal with heterogeneous samples on micrometer scale. Together with an online fluorescence mapping visualisation the optical alignment helps to optimize measuring procedures for combined microfocused X-ray techniques.

Keywords: micro focus, fluorescence, synchrotron
PACS: 01.30.Cc

INTRODUCTION

Investigation of heterogeneous samples with micrometer sized objects as they occur for example in environmental science [1] requires a careful offline pre-characterization with techniques like light microscopy and/or electron microscopy before applying synchrotron methods to achieve laterally resolved information on chemical and mineral properties of pollutants.

We have developed sample supports with four referencing cross lines of about 3 μm line widths to enable the transfer of sample positions and focusing parameters from a laboratory light microscope to the sample stage of a synchrotron experimental station (Fig. 1). There, automatically positioning macros for each pre-selected sample spot will be generated allowing rapidly moving the objects of interest into the synchrotron beam, and hence avoiding time consuming search for sample positions with built-in light microscopes at experimental stations which are usually of lower quality than the lab microscopes.

CP1092, *Synchrotron Radiation in Materials Science: 6th International Conference*, edited by R. Magalhaes-Paniago
© 2009 American Institute of Physics 978-0-7354-0625-4/09/$25.00

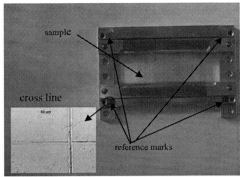

FIGURE 1. Sample holder with cross line marks for referencing sample positions

Fluorescence mappings using a newly developed online visualization program (based on IgorPro) show distributions of chemical elements (selectable by setting fluorescence regions) around the positions of interest (Fig. 2): A prerequisite to localize further positions for measuring X-ray absorption spectra and X-ray diffractograms to get information about chemical forms and mineral phases on a micrometer scale.

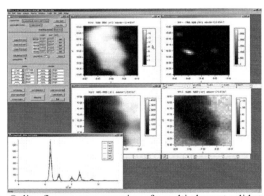

FIGURE 2. Online fluorescence mapping of a multi-element solid state detectors.

Both, the referencing and sample positioning system and the online fluorescence mapping were developed for the microfocus X-ray beamline of the Synchrotron Radiation Laboratory for Enviromental Studies (SUL-X), and will lead there to a more efficient use of synchrotron beam time. Moreover, the referencing and positioning system can be adapted to other instruments and enable exchange of samples while preserving the positions of marked objects, for example, between different microfocusing beamlines, e.g. synchrotron IR microscopy and hard X-ray microprobe beamlines.

POSITION REFERENCE SYSTEM

Any investigation of the sample needs to be done with a retracted experimental light microscope. In any other situation the microscope will hinder the fluorescence light and the fluorescence detector at a close position to the sample (fig. 3). Due to that requirement an effective temporary position database which references a certain position by name and allows a rapid relocation was implemented. An interruption for checking positions before starting the measurement can also be avoided. That database allows to import additional positions from an external position referencing system, e.g. the laboratory light microscope, if a minimal set of 4 reference points is defined for the experimental setup and the external laboratory system commonly.

Coordinates could be converted from the system of the laboratory light microscope into the system of the experimental stage by a common 3 dimensional transformation. Due to the small working distance of the laboratory light microscope the sample and the 4 reference marks (lu, ll, ru, rl in fig. 4) are positioned roughly in a plane. But approximately in-plane arranged reference marks result in a large uncertainty for the z-coordinate in case of a common 3 dimensional transformation.

To avoid this uncertainty the approach is to make use of the special geometric conditions of the assembly: The sample holder is placed to the laboratory light microscope in such a way, that the reference marks are located in a plane perpendicular to the direction of observation (z-stage).

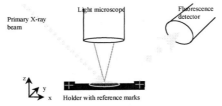

FIGURE 3. Schematic setup for fluorescence experiments at the SUL-X experimental station.

This means that the linear transformation can be described by the equation $TP_m + B = P_e$ (T is the transformation matrix, B is the transformation offset, P_m and P_e see fig. 4) with a specific feature that the z-coordinate of P_m is set to 0. The transformation in matrix notation is:

$$\begin{pmatrix} t_{00}x_m & t_{01}y_m \\ t_{10}x_m & t_{11}y_m \\ t_{20}y_m & t_{21}y_m \end{pmatrix} + \begin{pmatrix} b_x \\ b_y \\ b_z \end{pmatrix} = \begin{pmatrix} x_e \\ y_e \\ z_e \end{pmatrix}$$

As a result the number of parameters of the transformation reduces by 3 and the fourth reference point can be used to improve the accuracy.

To avoid the loss of the height of a point above the plane, which is virtually defined by the reference marks, a parameter (h) is derived from the input parameter set and handled as an offset to the z coordinate. The finally calculated coordinates in the experimental system are $P_e = (x_e, y_e, z_e + h)$. That simple correction by introducing the parameter h is justified by the special geometry of the setup.

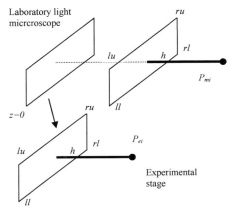

FIGURE 4. Schematic view at the coordinate transformation from the laboratory light microscope to the experimental stage.

The presented approach maximizes the amount of applicable beamtime (by decreasing the time for searching for regions of interest) and minimizes coordinate transformation errors. The practical application (see fig. 5) shows that the whole process leads to acceptable tolerances, which improves the operation of the microfocus experiments at SUL-X beamline.

(a)   (b)   (c)

FIGURE 5. Images of the same region of a sample (thin section of a rock) with different instruments. The region was selected with the laboratory light microscope (a). The same region observed after coordinate transformation with the built-in light microscope of the experimental station (b) and with online fluorescence mapping for Fe Kα radiation (c).

SUMMARY

A simplified transformation of external coordinates from objects selected with an offline microscope was introduced to the SUL-X microfocus beamline, which acts in combination with the new online fluorescence mapping as an effective tool for the investigation of heterogeneous samples.

REFERENCES

1. Göttlicher J. and Steininger R., "Synchrotron radiation laboratory for environmental studies" in *Book of abstracts*, The 19th International Congress on X-ray Optics and Microanalysis (ICXOM 2007), September 16-21, Kyoto, Japan, 2007, p. 141

Structure factor changes in supercooled yttria-alumina

Martin C. Wilding[1], G. Neville Greaves*[1], Quang Vu Van[1], Odile
Majérus[2] and Louis Hennet[3]

[1]Centre for Advanced Functional Materials and Devices
Institute of Mathematics and Physics, Aberystwyth University, Aberystwyth SY23 3BZ UK;
gng@aber.ac.uk
[2]Ecole nationale Supérieure de Chemie de paris, 11 rue Pierre et marie Curies, 75231, Paris, France.
[3]CNRS-CRMHT, 1d avenue de la Recherche Scietifique, 45071 Orléans cedex 9, France.

Abstract. Changes in the structure factor of yttria-alumina liquids have been identified in the supercooled range. Different inter-polyhedral configurations between AlO_4 and YO_6 groups distinguish low density and high density liquid phases. The coexistence of phases at high temperatures have been identified in simultaneous measurements of small angle x-ray scattering.

Keywords: Materials Science, Synchrotron Radiation
PACS: 81.00.00

INTRODUCTION

Polyamorphic phases of chemically identical composition are attracting increasing interest [1]. To date polyamorphism has been demonstrated in the solid state, particularly in tetrahedral systems like H_2O and Si under compression and decompression [1]. Evidence of polyamorphism at ambient pressures originating from the liquid state was discovered unexpectedly in glasses quenched from supercooled yttria-alumina liquids [2]. In particular polyamorphic unmixing was found for glasses with compositions between $Y_2Al_8O_{15}$ and $Y_3Al_5O_{12}$ (YAG). We report preliminary *in situ* x-ray scattering experiments where aerodynamic levitation laser-heated furnace techniques have been used to characterise these polyamorphs *in situ* for the first time.

EXPERIMENTAL ARRANGEMENT

In situ wide angle x-ray scattering (WAXS) from Y_2O_3-Al_2O_3 liquids was measured at 2500K with high energy 115kev X-rays on 11-ID-C at the APS. Diffuse scattering was collected directly from behind the sample over 10min periods. WAXS was also combined with SAXS using 16.9keV X-rays on station 6.2 at the SRS. SAXS/WAXS data was collected every 2min at temperatures down to 1515K, deep into the supercooled region, until homogeneous crystallisation took place [3].

CP1092, *Synchrotron Radiation in Materials Science: 6th International Conference*, edited by R. Magalhaes-Paniago
© 2009 American Institute of Physics 978-0-7354-0625-4/09/$25.00

For each of these experiments the refractory liquid samples were levitated on a stream of argon heated with a CO_2 laser from above. The temperature was recorded with a pyrometer also from the top of the drop, as illustrated for SRS experiments in Fig. 1. In this case WAXS was collected from the top of the drop and SAXS in transition, the X-rays being of sufficiently short wavelength to penetrate the 2mm diameter spheres. Incident and transmission ion chambers were used to maintain a constant I_T/I_0 in order to ensure that the drop was aligned at the same height in the X-ray beam. This was because the liquid sphere naturally rises in the levitator nozzle as the temperature rises and *vice versa*. A high speed camera (not shown) was used both as a diagnostic and also to detect sample rotation in the supercooled state and eventual crystallisation as the temperature was gradually lowered from the melting point at 2100K towards the glass transition expected around $2/3T_m$ at 1400K. In the event crystallisation took place close to 1520K

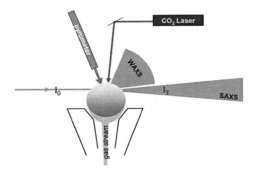

Figure 1. Schematic arrangement for recording SAXS/WAXS from an aerodynamic levitating laser heated drop.

RESULTS AND DISCUSSION

Structure factor data $S(Q)$ for liquid $Y_2Al_8O_{15}$ at 2500K obtained on 11-1D-C at the APS and the corresponding real space radial distribution function $g(r)$ are shown in Fig. 1 as an example. The large Q range available (up to $16Å^{-1}$) enabled the nearest neighbours, Al-O and Y-O at around 2Å, as well as the inter-cation correlations Al-Al, Al-Y and Y-Y between 2.5 and 3.5Å to be differentiated as can be seen in Fig. 2(b). The nearest neighbour and next nearest neighbour correlations evident in $g(r)$) are also identified in the other yttria-alumina liquids, but in proportions related to composition [3].

Where $S(Q)$ is concerned, detailed computer simulations (RMC and MD) from quenched glasses [1,4] reveal that the inter-polyhedral arrangements that are parameterised by the Al-Y and Y-Y partials make the largest contribution to the principle peak (PP) close to $2Å^{-1}$ in Fig. 2(a). They are inevitably also mixed in with Al-O, Y-O and O-O correlations in the second broad peak between 3 and $4Å^{-1}$. This modelling can also be used to inform the new results on Y_2O_3-Al_2O_3 liquids [3]. In particular large MC models have shown that the overall structures of these binary glasses are not totally uniform but that there is a preference for clustering of yttria polyhedra within a mainly tetrahedral alumina matrix [4]. This microsegregation of yttria in Y_2O_3-Al_2O_3 glasses is similar to percolating channel formation in silicate glasses [5] – the so-called modified random network. Interestingly as the yttria content increases in Y_2O_3-Al_2O_3 glasses there is a gradual conversion of edge-sharing to corner-sharing configurations between neighbouring yttria polyhedra. This coincides with a stiffening of the structure suggesting that the originating liquids might be becoming stronger.

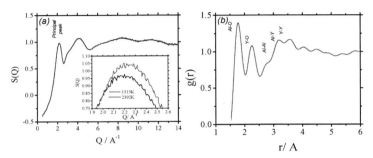

Figure 2. (a) Structure factor $S(Q)$ for liquid $Y_2Al_8O_{15}$ at 2500K measured with high energy x-rays. Insert shows reversible changes in the principle peak at lower temperatures. (b) Fourier transformed real space structure, $g(r)$.

In situ SAXS-WAXS experiments conducted in the supercooled region on MPW6.2 at the SRS [3] have identified significant changes in the position and intensity of the PP in $S(Q)$ with temperature, as shown by the inset in Fig. 2(a). Importantly these realignments around 2Å^{-1} shown for 1515K and 2392K are reversible. The difference structure factor $\Delta S(Q)$ also reveals correlated swings in features in the second peak in $S(Q)$ which are centred around 3.3Å^{-1} and 4.0Å^{-1} which can be associated with Y-Y and Al-Y partials respectively [3]. Specifically Al-Y features move to higher Q and Y-Y features to lower Q as the temperature reduces from 2392K to 1515K.

Importantly, all of these changes in WAXS patterns also coincide with an increase in SAXS intensity below 0.1Å^{-1}. Moreover the peak in the integrated SAXS can be attributed to the coexistence of low and high density supercooled liquid phases [3]. Liquid unmixing was previously estimated from *ex situ* measurements on rapidly quenched yttria-alumina glasses to occur at temperatures around 250° lower [2]. This emphasizes the importance of making structural measurements of polyamorphism *in situ* in the liquid state rather extrapolating from quench rate conditions.

From detailed structure factor analysis of yttria-alumina glasses [4] associates the shift of the PP around 2.2Å^{-1} in supercooled $Y_2Al_8O_{15}$, which can be clearly seen for the *in situ* liquid in Fig. 2(a) together with changes in the second peak between 3Å^{-1} and 4Å^{-1}, with a shortening of Al-Y distances and with an accompanying increase in

Y-Y distances. Indeed we can estimate the Al-Y and Y-Y interaction distances in the lower temperature low density phase from $\Delta r_{AB} = r_{AB}\Delta Q_{AB} / Q_{AB}$, where r_{AB} and Q_{AB} are the corresponding cation separation and position of the wavevector feature for the higher temperature high density phase whose $S(Q)$ is illustrated in Fig. 2(a).

These inter-polyhedral changes are associated in 3D models obtained from MD and RMC simulations [4] with increased cation clustering in the low density phase compared to the high density phase. The configurational change is illustrated in Fig. 3. In particular this involves increased numbers of corner-sharing polyhedra and is consistent with the lower entropy expected for this density driven transition [1]. Molten alumina is largely tetrahedral [5] with most oxygens present as triclusters (OAl_3). We suppose, therefore, that for supercooled yttria-alumina liquids the shortening of Al-Y distances for AY20 between HDL and LDL (Fig. 3) may be due to the break up of tricluster OAl_3 groups.

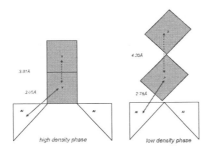

Figure 3. Configurational change found in liquid $Y_2Al_8O_{15}$ either side of the HDL-LDL transformation, Al-Y distances decreasing and Y-Y distances increasing due to switches from edge to corner sharing arrangements.

REFERENCES

1. P.F. McMillan, M. Wilson, M.C. Wilding, D. Daisenberger, M. Mezouar and G.N. Greaves, *J. Phys.: Condens. Matter* **19**, 415101 (2007)
2. S. Aasland and P.F. McMillan: *Nature* **369**, 633 (1994)
3. G.N. Greaves, M.C. Wilding, S. Fearn, D. Langstaff, F. Kargl, S. Cox, O. Majérus, Q. Vu Van, C.J. Benmore, R. Weber, C.M. Martin and L. Hennet, *Science* **322**, 566 (2008)
4. M.C. Wilding, M. Wilson and P.F. McMillan: Phil. Trans. R. Soc. A **363**, 598 (2005)
5. G.N. Greaves and S. Sen, *Adv. Phys.* **56**, 1 (2007)

High Resolution PDF Measurements on Ag Nanoparticles

Túlio C. R. Rocha[a, b], Chris Martin[c], Stefan Kycia[c] and <u>Daniela Zanchet</u>[a]*

*a Brazilian Synchrotron Light Laboratory, Laboratório Nacional de Luz Síncrotron
Síncrotron, CP 6192, 13083-971, Campinas SP, Brazil*
b Universidade Estadual de Campinas
c University of Guelph
Corresponding author: fax: (55) 19-3512-1004, e-mail: zanchet@lnls.br.

Abstract. The quantitative analysis of structural defects in Ag nanoparticles was addressed in this work. We performed atomic scale structural characterization by a combination of x-ray diffraction (XRD) using the Pair Distribution Function analysis (PDF) and High Resolution Transmission Electron Microscopy (HRTEM). The XRD measurements were performed using an innovative instrumentation setup to provide high resolution PDF patterns

Keywords: PDF, XRD, Silver, Nanoparticle, CHESS,
PACS: 61.46.Hk

INTRODUCTION

The knowledge of the atomic scale structure is a prerequisite to understanding material properties and traditionally, x-ray diffraction has been successful in obtaining this information. However, in the case of nanostructured materials, quantitative information about the atomic structures is not accessible by conventional methods originally designed for bulk crystalline materials. Particularly, in the case of noble metal nanoparticles (Au and Ag), the quantitative structural characterization is challenging because the very small crystallite sizes cause extreme diffraction peak broadening for these samples. In this work, we begin to tackle the question of the quantitative analysis of structural defects in Ag nanoparticles by a combination HRTEM with XRD data analysis using the PDF formalism.

RESULTS AND DISCUSSION

Ag nanoparticles samples were synthesized using the methodology described in ref 1 under different concentrations of O_2, since the presence of O_2 is known to affect the structure of the nanoparticles. The samples were first characterized by HRTEM and synchrotron XRD in the Brazilian Synchrotron Light Laboratory . A HRTEM image

CP1092, *Synchrotron Radiation in Materials Science: 6th International Conference*, edited by R. Magalhaes-Paniago
© 2009 American Institute of Physics 978-0-7354-0625-4/09/$25.00

is shown in figure 1, where a Ag nanoparticle with nearly 9 nm in diameter is shown with many parallel structural defects (twin planes and stacking faults). The qualitative comparison of the x-ray diffractograms (not shown) indicated that the samples presented different populations of defective particles depending on the amount of O_2 presented in the synthesis solution, with sample synthesized in lower concentrations of O_2 presenting less defective particles.

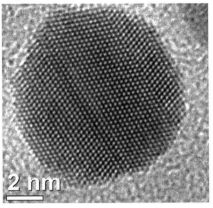

Figure 1 – HRTEM image of single Ag nanoparticle presenting many parallel structural defects

In order to obtain quantitative data for a distribution of defective particles, we performed diffraction experiments at Cornell High Energy Synchrotron Source, Ithaca, New York, using 60 keV x-rays. Diffraction curves were obtained up to high Q values (40 or 50Å^{-1}) to perform pair distribution function analysis. The measurements were performed using a new experimental setup exploiting the high flux of high energy x-rays of the CHESS A2 wiggler beam line with cryostat cooled samples and an energy dispersive 5 element solid state detector, which was scanned to cover a wide range of the reciprocal space. This approach allowed us to obtain diffraction curves out to high Q values, with very good statistics, no Compton scattering contamination thus resulting in high resolution PDF pattern.

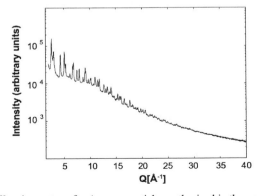

Figure 2 – Diffraction pattern for Ag nanoparticle synthesized in the presence of nitrogen

103

The diffraction pattern shown in figure 2 is a representative raw pattern, taken from a single detector. Even at this stage, it is clear that the data extends beyond the Q range of in-house diffractometers (~8 Å for Cu Kα, and ~13.5 Å for Mo Kα). This is further emphasized in examination of the interference function, since the atomic scattering factor is divided out and the data is multiplied by Q, increasing the significance of the high Q data. As shown in figure 3, the signal does not get drowned out by noise past 30 Å.

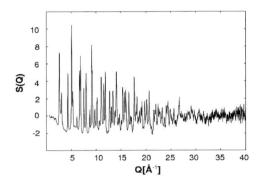

Figure 3 – Interference function for Ag nanoparticle synthesized in the presence of nitrogen

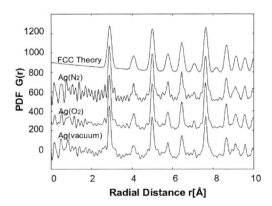

Figure 4 – PDF for three Ag nanoparticles synthesized under different conditions, as well as that predicted by theory for a FCC crystal

In figure 4 we see the PDF for the three different silver nanoparticles, as well as a theoretical PDF based solely on a FCC crystal structure. It is clearly visible that all three nanoparticles exhibit a strong FCC structure, with a lattice constant of 4.077 ± 0.005 Å, with no significant deviation in the first few nearest neighbour peaks. From the PDF analysis we are also able to identify the effective average size of the nanoparticles, which in this case appears to be approximately 6.0 nm, significantly less than the 9nm determined by TEM. This is likely due not to a discrepancy in actual particle size, but rather a further indication of the presence of stacking faults in the samples, resulting in a smaller crystallographic size than physical size. A detailed analysis is now being performed to fully extract the information in these diffraction patterns.

CONCLUSIONS

By using high resolution PDF analysis and diffraction data out to sufficiently high Q values, with good statistics, combined with HRTEM images complex information about defects distribution on Ag nanoparticles have been tackled. Despite the presence of a large quantity of crystal defects in the particles, the resulting PDF showed a very good agreement with FCC crystal structure, and allowed the determination of the lattice constant good to 0.1%. Although the defects did not significantly change the qualitative appearance of the PDF, the effective crystallographic size shows evidence of these defects. Further analysis is required to accurately quantify the differences in defects among samples, and HRTEM observations will then be used to construct structural models to compare with these PDF results.

ACKNOWLEDGMENTS

The authors wish to thank Alexander Kazimirov and the CHESS and LNLS staff for their assistance. LNLS and CHESS are also acknowledged for the use of their facilities HRTEM (LME–LNLS) and XRD (XRD2 and XPD beam lines–LNLS and A2 wiggler beam line–CHESS) experiments

REFERENCES

1. T.C.R. Rocha; H. Winnischofer; E. Westphal; D. Zanchet "Formation Kinetics of Silver Triangular Nanoplates" *J. Phys. Chem. C* **111**, 2885 (2007).
2. Petkov, V.; Jeong, I-K.; Chung, J. S.; Thorpe, M. F.; Kycia, S.; Billinge, S. J. L. "High Real-Space Resolution Measurement of the Local Structure of Ga 1-xIn xAs Using X-Ray Diffraction" *Phys. Rev. Lett.* **83**, 4089-4092 (1997).

Quantification of Multilayer Samples by Confocal µXRF

R. Daniel Pérez[a,b,c], H. J. Sánchez[a,b,c], C. A. Pérez[d] and M. Rubio[a,b,c]

[a]Facultad de Matemática Astronomía y Física, Universidad Nacional de Córdoba, Ciudad Universitaria, Córdoba (5000), Argentina.
[b] CONICET, Rivadavia 1917, Buenos Aires (1033), Argentina
[c]CEPROCOR, Ministerio de Ciencia y Tecnología de Córdoba, Santa María de Punilla (5164), Córdoba, Argentina.
[d] Laboratório Nacional de Luz Síncrotron – LNLS, POB6192, 13084-97 Campinas, SP, Brasil.

Abstract. The confocal setup consists of x-ray lenses in the excitation as well as in the detection channel. In this configuration, a micro volume defined by the overlap of the foci of both x-ray lenses is analyzed. Scanning this micro volume through the sample, 1-3 dimensional studies can be performed. For intermediate thin homogeneous layers a scanning in the normal direction to the surface sample provides information of its thickness and elemental composition. For multilayer samples it also provides the order of each layer in the stratified structure. For the confocal setup, we used a glass monocapillary in the excitation channel and a monolithic half polycapillary in the detection channel. The experiment was carried out at the D09B beamline of the LNLS using white beam. In the present work, a new algorithm was applied to analyze in detail by confocal µXRF a sample of three paint layers on a glass substrate. Using the proposed algorithm, information about thickness and elemental densities was obtained for each layer of these samples.

Keywords: X-ray microanalysis, confocal, XRF, quantification.
PACS: 82.80.Ej

INTRODUCTION

A model for the theoretical description of x-ray fluorescence intensity registered by confocal µXRF was introduced by Malzer and Kanngießer in 2005 [1]. These authors showed that the sensitivity in confocal µXRF is not constant in the probing volume, but it has a three dimensional profile described by a Gaussian function. To quantify multilayer samples, linear scans of the x-ray fluorescence emission through a normal direction of the surface are usually done. This scan is theoretically described by the spatial convolution of the sensitivity and the x-ray fluorescence emission rate to the detector. Using this theoretical framework we developed a new algorithm to quantify multilayers samples by confocal setup. In the present paper, an application of the new algorithm is shown.

CP1092, *Synchrotron Radiation in Materials Science: 6th International Conference*, edited by R. Magalhaes-Paniago

MATERIALS AND METHODS

Instrumentation. The experiment was carried out in the DO09B beamline of the Synchrotron Light National Laboratory (Laboratório Nacional de Luz Síncrotron, LNLS) using white beam [2]. A silicon drift x-ray detector with 150 eV of resolution at 5.9 keV was positioned perpendicular to the photon beam on the horizontal plane. This system was mounted on a motorized XYZ stage. Suspended from the snout of the silicon drift detector, a fixed holder holds a half monolythic polycapillary with its optical axes centered and normal to the window of the detector. This polycapillary has a focal distance of 20 mm with a focal dimension of 75 mm and a transmission efficiency of 5 %. A complete description of this lens can be found in a previous paper [3]. In the excitation channel a conical glass monocapillary was mounted in a special motorized gimbal. The distance from the output of the monocapillary to the focal spot of the half monolithic polycapillary was 15 mm. The transmission efficiency of the monocapillary for white beam is 34 %. Transmission dependence with the incident energy was determined previously by means of a simulation program. A complete description of this lens can be found elsewhere [4]. Samples were mounted vertically at 45° of the incident direction on a motorized XYZ sample stage. The spatial resolution of this device is 0.6 mm.

Aligned ionising chambers at the entrance of the monocapillary and behind the sample holder were used to align efficiently the monocapillary. In addition, a CCD camera was placed behind the sample holder to determine the position of the incident beam. A digital optical microscope focused on the sample was employed to distinguish details on the area excited by the incident beam.

Measurement and calibration of confocal μXRF. To calibrate the confocal m-XRF setup, we perform linear scans through normal direction of pure foils. We used standard (Alfa Aesar) thin foils of V, Fe and Cu with high purity (99.9%) and known thickness. For Pb we used a thick foil of 2 mm thickness and high purity. For all scans, the counting live-time for each point was 10 s/step and the step size was 10 μm. For all elements except Pb we followed the Kα x-ray fluorescent line (see Figure 1). For Pb we followed the Lα x-ray fluorescent line.

Once the calibration was established, we perform a quantitative analysis by confocal μXRF of Ti, Cr, Fe and Pb in three alkyd enamel layers painted on a glass substrate. Ti was present in the middle layer; Cr, Fe and Pb were present in the outside layer; and Fe and Pb were present in the deepest layer. Figure 2 shows the linear scan for Fe present in the outside layer. The thickness of each layer was measured at several points of the layer with an outside micrometer.

THEORY

Fluorescent Intensity. For a polychromatic source the intensity of a specific x-ray line can be written as:

$$Ip_i(x) = A \int_0^{E_m} \rho_i I_0(E) \tau_{F,i}(E) \left(\int_0^D \eta_i(E, x'-x) \exp(-\tilde{\mu}_i(E)x') \, dx' \right) dE \tag{1}$$

where E_m is the maximum energy of the incoming photons, A is an experimental factor, I_0 is the incoming photon flux of energy E, ρ_i is the density (in g/cm^3) of the i-element in the sample, $\tau_{F,i}$ is the production cross section (in cm^2/g) for the respective x-ray line of the i-element at energy E, η_i is the sensitivity profile of the spectrometer for the i-element, and $\tilde{\mu}_i$ is the effective linear mass attenuation coefficient at energy E for the i-element defined as follows:

$$\tilde{\mu}_i = \sum_{j=1}^{r} \rho_j \left(\frac{\mu_j(E)}{\sin(\theta_0)} + \frac{\mu_j(E_i)}{\sin(\theta_1)} \right) \tag{2}$$

where ρ_j is the density of the j-element, μ_j is the mass attenuation coefficient (in cm^2/g) of the j-element at energy E, E_i is the energy of the x-ray line of the i-element, θ_0 and θ_1 are the medium angle of the impinging beam and detected beam respectively.

Quantification algorithm. The quantification algorithm is an iterative procedure applied to thin intermediate layers where the x-ray fluorescent radiation has an exponential attenuation. The iterative process is based on the following equation:

$$(\rho_i D)_n = \frac{\int_{-\infty}^{+\infty} I_i(x) \, dx}{A \, C_{n-1}} \, , \tag{3}$$

with
$$C_{n-1} = \int_0^{E_m} \tau_{F,i}(E) I_0(E) \left[\frac{(1 - \exp(-\tilde{\mu}_i(E) D))}{\tilde{\mu}_i(E) D} \right]_{n-1} dE \tag{4}$$

RESULTS AND DISCUSSION

The paint layers studied in the experiments had a high amount of an alkyd resin as an organic vehicle composed firstly by light elements. Since these elements cannot be detected by our confocal geometry, the volumetric densities of them had to be determined using the bulk volumetric density. Table 1 shows the densities obtained for Ti, Cr, Fe and Pb in the paint layers with the proposed algorithm. Each result was obtained with only ten iterations. The density values correspond approximately with the expected values for an alkyd resin. Further research in the accuracy of the algorithm will be carry out in the near future.

TABLE 1. Elemental volumetric densities obtained in a multilayer sample by confocal μXRF. ND: Not detectable.

Layer	Ti [g/cm³]	Cr [g/cm3]	Fe [g/cm³]	Pb [g/cm³]
1	ND	0.045	0.028	0.032
2	0.060	ND	ND	ND
3	ND	ND	0.070	0.041

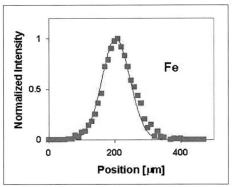

FIGURE 1. Experimental points and fitting curve of the Fe-linear scan of a pure iron thin foil (0.1mm thickness) by confocal μXRF.

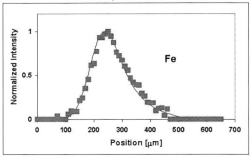

FIGURE 2. Experimental points and fitting curve of the Fe-linear scan of a green paint layer in a multilayer sample (outside layer) by confocal μXRF.

ACKNOWLEDGMENTS

The authors would like to thank the financial support from the Brazilian Synchrotron Light Source (Under proposal LNLS D09B-XRF-5744/06 and D09B-XRF-6512/07); CONICET, CEPROCOR and FaMAF from Argentina.

REFERENCES

1. W. Malzer and B. Kanngieber. *Spectrochim. Acta* **B60**, 1334-1341 (2005).

2. C. A. Perez, M. Radtke, H. J. Sanchez, H. Tolentino, R. T. Neuenshwander, W. Barg, M. Rubio, M. Bueno, I. M. Raimundo, J. Rohwedder. *X-Ray Spectrom.* **28**, 320 (1999).
3. R. D. Pérez, H. J. Sánchez, M. Rubio, C. A. Pérez. Characterization of home-made x-ray polycapillaries. *X-Ray Spectrom.* Accepted for publication (2008).
4. H. J.. Sánchez and C. A. Pérez. *J. Trace and Microprobe technique* **16**, 501 (1998).

In situ XAS studies of Pt_xPd_{1-x} nanoparticles under thermal annealing

F. Bernardi[1], M. C. M. Alves[2] and J. Morais[1]

[1] *Instituto de Física, Universidade Federal do Rio Grande do Sul (UFRGS), Avenida Bento Gonçalves, 9500, Bairro Agronomia, CP 15051, CEP 91501-970, Porto Alegre, RS, Brazil*
[2] *Instituto de Química, Universidade Federal do Rio Grande do Sul (UFRGS), Avenida Bento Gonçalves, 9500, Bairro Agronomia, CP 15003, CEP 91501-970, Porto Alegre, RS, Brazil*

Abstract. In this work, we have studied Pt_xPd_{1-x} (x = 1, 0.7 or 0.5) nanoparticles subjected to H_2 reduction and sulfidation under H_2S atmosphere, both at 300 °C. The system was studied by in-situ x-ray absorption spectroscopy (in-situ XAS). We observed that the efficiency of sulfidation is directly proportional to the quantity of Pd atoms in the nanoparticle, provided the reduction process has been achieved.

Keywords: Pt-Pd, sulfur, nanoparticles, XAS, EXAFS, sulfidation.
PACS: 61.05.cj, 81.16.Hc.

INTRODUCTION

Metallic nanoparticles have been used as catalysts in various industrial processes. It is well known that in bimetallic systems the addition of a second metal provides a method for controlling the catalytic activity and selectivity through cooperative effects. Studies on the sulfidation of Pt and Pt-Pd catalysts are mainly related to supported catalysts such as Pt/Al_2O_3 or SiO_2 and $PtPd/Al_2O_3$ or SiO_2 [1-3]. Few studies are addressed to non-supported nanoparticles [4, 5]. The majority of the studies on PtPd nanoparticles are concerned with the systems in the as prepared and reduced conditions [5, 6]. In this work we have studied Pt_xPd_{x-1} nanoparticles before and after they were submitted to reduction and sulfidation thermal treatments. We show that the nanoparticle composition is a key factor to determine the amount of sulfur that is adsorbed (or chemisorbed) by the catalyst. For this, we have mainly used in situ x-ray absorption spectroscopy (XAS), which is widely used to characterize the structural and electronic properties of catalysts.

RESULTS AND DISCUSSION

CP1092, *Synchrotron Radiation in Materials Science: 6th International Conference*, edited by R. Magalhaes-Paniago
© 2009 American Institute of Physics 978-0-7354-0625-4/09/$25.00

The PtPd nanoparticles were prepared with 1-n-butyl-3-methylimidazolium hexafluorophosphate (BMI.PF$_6$) ionic liquid, as described elsewhere [7, 8]. The nanoparticles were compacted in the form of pellets for the in-situ XAS studies, in the transmission mode, at the XAFS1 beamline of LNLS (Campinas, Brazil) [9]. We have investigated the L$_3$ edge of Pt as the sample was submitted to thermal treatments under gaseous environment. The sample treatment was achieved using a dedicated reactor built by our group that allows a controlled heat of the sample under gas flow [4]. For these experiments, the system was reduced at 573K during 20 min under 78 % He + 22 % H$_2$ flux and, then, exposed to the sulfidation process by a flux of 75 % He + 21 % H$_2$ + 4 % H$_2$S for 30 min. The XAS spectra were acquired *in situ* at the end of each step, i.e., reduction and sulfidation.

Figure 1 summarizes the XAS results for the Pt$_{0.5}$Pd$_{0.5}$ nanoparticles. It suggests that the nanoparticles in the as prepared form are oxidized at the surface. After treatment under H$_2$ the nanoparticles are completely reduced. The sulfidation process starts after Pt$_x$Pd$_{1-x}$ reduction under the conditions described above. The sulfidation was not observed on non-reduced samples. After the sulfidation, one observes the edge shift towards higher energies and modifications in the interatomic distances. The Pt-Pd distance in the alloy is about. Despite of the large core hole width for Pt at the L$_3$ edge (5.31 eV) one observes the tendency of the edge value that is lower for the reduced sample and higher for the sulfided one [6]. The attenuated amplitudes observed in the EXAFS and FT of the Pt$_{0.5}$Pd$_{0.5}$ nanoparticles are compatible with the low dimensionality of the system. The sulfidation process leads to a complete different local structure around the Pt atoms, where the metal-metal contribution is very weak. This is due to the fact that up to k range of 10 Å^{-1} the scattering amplitude of Pt-S is much higher than that of Pt-Pt or Pt-Pd bond. We have observed that, once the reduction is achieved, the sulfur incorporation increases proportionally with the amount of Pd in the alloy. The Pt-S bond originated after the sulfidation process is clearly observed and corresponds to the peak about 1.8 Å (without phase shift correction). We have also performed in situ dispersive-XAS (DXAS) and x-ray photoelectron spectroscopy (XPS) studies on these samples and the results (not shown here) corroborate the XAS results.

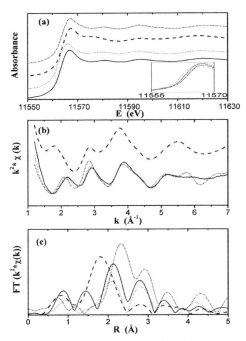

FIGURE 1 – (a) XANES spectra at the Pt L_3 edge of the $Pt_{0.5}Pd_{0.5}$ nanoparticles. The inset shows a zoom of the edge region. (b) EXAFS signals, χ (k), and (c) the corresponding Fourier transforms: as prepared (full line), after reduction under H_2 (dot line), after the sulfidation process (dash line) and the Pt standard (dash dot line).

CONCLUSION

In this work, we have used an especially designed reactor for in situ XAS measurements that can be applied in heterogeneous catalysis characterization. The reactor was applied to investigate the reduction and the sulfidation processes of catalysts consisted of Pt_xPd_{1-x} nanoparticles. We were able to follow the environment modifications in the short range order around the Pt atoms as the catalysts were submitted to thermal reactions. The nanoparticle catalysts have demonstrated interesting results such as high reactivity with S, which depends on the amount of Pd n the alloy.

ACKNOWLEDGMENTS

We thank the support given by the LNLS staff. Work funded by CNPq, CAPES, and LNLS (XAFS1 5269, XAFS1 5695). F. B. thanks CNPq for his PhD fellowship.

REFERENCES

1. Bando K. K.; Kawai T.; Asakura K.; Matsui T.; Bihan L. L.; Yasuda H.; Yoshimura Y.; Oyama S. T.; *Cat. Today*, 2006, **111**, 199-204.
2. Kobayashi J.; Shimizu T.; Mizushima T. *Bul. of the Chem Soc. of Japan* 2000, **73(10)**, 2395-2401.
3. Appay M-D.; Manoli J-M.; Potvin C.; Muhler M.; Wild U.; Pozdnyakova O.; Paál Z.; *J. Catal.* 2004, **222**, 419-428.
4. Bernardi F.; Alves M. C. M.; Scheeren C. W.; Dupont J.; Morais J. *J. Elec. Spec. and Rel. Phen.*, 2007, **156-158**, 186-190.
5. Chen, C.-H.; Hwang, B.-J.; Wang, G.-R.; Sarma, L. S.; Tang, M.-T.; Liu, D.-G.; Lee, J.-F. *J. Phys. Chem. B.* 2005, **109**, 21566-21575.
6. Cho, S. J.; Kang, S. K.; *Cat. Today*, 2004, **93-95**, 561-566.
7. Dupont, J.; de Souza, R. F. ; Suarez, P. A. Z. *Chem. Rev.,* 2002, **102**, 3667-3692.
8. Scheeren, C. W.; Machado, G.; Teixeira, S. R.; Morais, J.; Domingos, J. B.; Dupont, J., *J. Phys. Chem. B,* 2006, **110**, 13011-13020.
9. Tolentino, H. C. N.; Ramos, A. Y.; Alves, M. C. M.; Barrea, R. A.; Tamura, E.; Cezar, J. C.; Watanabe, N.; *J. Synch. Rad.,* 2001, **8**, 1040-1046.

Micro/Nanomanufacturing in Support of Materials Science

L.K. Jian[a], H.O. Moser[a,b], A. Chen[a], S.P. Heussler[a], G. Liu[a], Shahrain bin Mahmood[a], S.M.P. Kalaiselvi[a], S.M. Maniam[a], Selven Virasawmy[a], Y.P. Ren[a], M.D. Barrett[b], A.L. Dhanapaul[b]

[a]Singapore Synchrotron Light Source (SSLS)
National University of Singapore
5 Research Link, Singapore 117603

[b]Department of Physics, National University of Singapore
2 Science Drive, Singapore 117542

Abstract. With its LiMiNT facility (Lithography for Micro- and Nanotechnology), Singapore Synchrotron Light Source (SSLS) provides a one-stop shop for micro/nano fabrication on large areas (typically 4" diameter). Synchrotron deep X-ray lithography, eventually enhanced by the super-resolution process, is used to simultaneously pattern large numbers of micro/nano structures into a resist. Laser direct writer or electron beam serve as primary pattern generators, in particular, for mask making. Structure heights of >1mm, aspect ratios of >200, and minimum sizes of <200 nm have been achieved, not necessarily simultaneously. Such structures may be replicated into a variety of metals and plastics. Tilting, rotating of the mask-substrate stack during exposure enables the parallel production of nearly 3D structures. Application fields include electromagnetic metamaterials, X-ray and infrared optics, photonics, lasers, quantum technology, precision manufacturing, and fluidics. SSLS is serving a growing community of users and customers.

Keywords: Micro/nanofabrication, synchrotron, metamaterial, atom trap, photonic crystal
PACS: 07.85.Qe, 41.20.Jb, 42.55.Tv, 81.07.-b

INTRODUCTION

Singapore Synchrotron Light Source (SSLS) is operating a comprehensive one-stop facility named LiMiNT for Lithography for Micro and Nanotechnology. Including deep X-ray lithography with synchrotron radiation, the LIGA process (German acronym for deep X-ray lithography, electroplating, and molding) [1] is known to enable the production of high-aspect-ratio micro/nanostructures with vertical dimensions ranging from micrometers to millimeters and horizontal dimensions reaching down to the nanoscale. Current application fields include electromagnetic metamaterials, X-ray and infrared optics, photonics, lasers, quantum technology, precision manufacturing, and fluidics. In this paper, some new and novel application examples are presented that support the characterization and development of materials [2] [3].

CP1092, *Synchrotron Radiation in Materials Science: 6th International Conference*, edited by R. Magalhaes-Paniago
© 2009 American Institute of Physics 978-0-7354-0625-4/09/$25.00

LIMINT FACILITY

The LiMiNT beamline provides useful photon flux at sample from 2 to >10 keV for (deep) X-ray lithography. It is connected to the Helios 2 storage ring. The end station is an Oxford Danfysik scanner (Fig. 1). X-ray masks as well as optical masks are fabricated in-house. The optical mask fabrication is carried out with a Heidelberg Instruments DWL 66 direct-write laser system with 20 mm and 4 mm writing heads for minimum structure sizes 5 μm and 1 μm. A typical X-ray mask is fabricated based on a graphite wafer of 200 μm thickness and 100 mm diameter as a membrane on which a 30 μm thick layer of SU-8 resist is spin coated. The pattern of the optical mask is transferred to the SU-8 resist layer by UV exposure in an MA8/BA6 mask aligner. Then, a 20 μm gold absorber layer is deposited into the SU-8 mould by electroplating. The graphite membrane with the patterned gold absorber is then glued on an aluminum NIST-standard mask holder ring. Fig. 2 shows examples of the optical and X-ray masks.

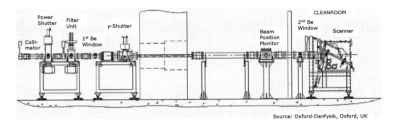

FIGURE 1. LiMiNT beamline for deep X-ray lithography

FIGURE 2. In-house fabrication of optical mask (left) and X-ray mask (right). The useful area is 80 mm in diameter.

MICRO/NANOFABRICATION

Micro/nanofabrication of metamaterials

Electromagnetic metamaterials (EM³) feature small engineered metal structures, densely distributed in space, that exhibit negative dielectric permittivity and magnetic permeability within a resonant frequency band. Under such conditions, the material has a negative refractive index and may rekindle evanescent waves, unusual phenomena that entail potential applications like sub-wavelength resolution imaging and invisibility cloaking. EM³ produced at SSLS are resonant at THz frequencies. Fig. 3 shows structures that are composed of split rings and rods made of Au or Ni as well as split cylinders[4-9].

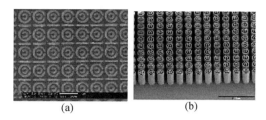

(a)   (b)

FIGURE 3. Au rod-split-ring nanostructures fabricated by e beam writing and sputter deposition (a, scale bar 1 µm) and high-aspect-ratio split cylinders fabricated by laser writing and X-ray lithography (b, scale bar 500 µm)

Fabrication of micro-magnetic traps

Magnetic fields generated by current-carrying wires can trap atoms. Using micro-fabrication techniques, such traps can be made extremely small, and large complex arrays of traps can be fabricated onto a single chip. Fig 4 shows two types of micro-magnetic traps (MMT). Lithography processes are essential to the fabrication of both traps, type I (X-ray lithography, tall HAR trap, Fig. 4a) and type II (UV lithography, flat trap, Fig. 4b). MMTs are used for holding Rb atoms in place for experiments related to quantum technology [10].

  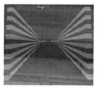 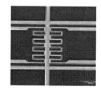

FIGURE 4a. Micro-magnetic trap I, 100 µm thick gold structures with 30 µm feature size. Chip size 5x5 cm² AlN substrate (left), SEM close-up, scale bar 200 µm (right)

FIGURE 4b. Micro-magnetic trap II, gold structures with 5 µm feature size. Chip size 5x5cm² SiO₂/Si substrate (left), SEM close-up, scale bar 200 µm (right)

Nanofabrication of photonic crystal materials

2D photonic crystal structures in PMMA have been fabricated by X-ray lithography (Figure 5). The X-ray masks used are 1µm thick SiN membranes with 300 nm thick Au absorbers, produced by electron-beam lithography (EBL) and electroplating. The EBL processes are optimized for the pattern generation with sub-100 nm resolution in polymethylmethacrylate (PMMA) [11].

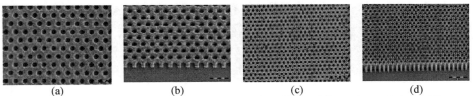

FIGURE 5. 2D gold photonic crystal structures as absorber of X-ray lithography mask (a, b); 2D photonic crystal structures fabricated in PMMA by X-ray lithography (c, d). Scale bars 2 μm in (a, c) and 1 μm in (b,d)

CONCLUSIONS

The LiMiNT facility of Singapore Synchrotron Light Source (SSLS) provides a one-stop shop for micro/nano fabrication. With its capabilities in e beam and laser writing, deep X-ray lithography, electroplating, and hot embossing, LiMiNT has been supporting materials-related research in various fields including metamaterials, quantum technology, and photonic crystals.

ACKNOWLEDGMENTS

Work performed at SSLS under NUS Core Support C-380-003-003-001, A*STAR/MOE RP 3979908M and A*STAR 12 105 0038 grants.

REFERENCES

1. E.W. Becker, W. Ehrfeld, P. Hagmann, A. Maner, D. Muenchmeyer, Microelectron. Eng. 4(1986)35
2. H. O. Moser, L. K. Jian, et al., MRS_S OUTLOOK, V2, N1 (2007), 11, http://www.mrs.org.sg
3. L. K. Jian, H. O. Moser, et al. , Journal of Physics: Conference Series 34(2006): International MEMS Conference , 891
4. V. G. Veselago, Sov. Phys. Usp. 10, 509 (1968)
5. J. B. Pendry, A. J. Holden, D. J. Robbins, and W. J. Stewart, IEEE Trans. Microwave Theory Tech. 47,2075 (1999)
6. D. R. Smith, W. J. Padilla, D. C. Vier, S. C. Nemat-Nasser, and S. Schultz, Phys. Rev. Lett. 84, 4184 (2000)
7. H. O. Moser, B. D. F. Casse, O. Wilhelmi, B. T. Saw, Phys. Rev. Lett. 94, 063901 (2005)
8. N. M. Litchinitser, V. M. Shalaev, The McGraw-Hill 2008 Yearbook of Science & Technology, 230
9. H. O. Moser et al., this conference.
10. M. D. Barrett, Ultra-cold atom, http://coldatom.quantumlah.org/index.html
11. A. Chen, G. Liu, L. K. Jian, H. O. Moser, COSMOS, V.3, N.1, 79 (2007)

SAXS study of optically homogeneous silica glass synthesized by flame aerosol method

Juliana Santiago dos Santos, Eduardo Ono, and Carlos Kenichi Suzuki*

UNICAMP-State University of Campinas, Department of Materials Engineering, CP. 6122, Campinas-SP, Brazil, suzuki@fem.unicamp.br, Phone: +55-19-3521-3337, Fax: +55-19-3289-3722

Abstract. Aiming the development of optically homogeneous silica glass for use on photonic components, in this research, silica boules were synthesized by the VAD (Vapor-phase Axial Deposition) flame aerosol method by varying the H_2/O_2 ratio. Radial structure of sintered silica samples were characterized by small-angle X-ray scattering technique in correlation with its optical properties, refractive index radial homogeneity and birefringence. The refractive index was determined by interferometry and optical spectrometry. The polarization spectrophotometry was used to obtain the birefringence. The structural radial homogeneity in sintered silica glass presents strong correlation with optical properties. Also, silica glass with high radial homogeneity of refractive index of 1 ppm and birefringence of 2 nm/cm can be synthesized by controlling the H_2/O_2 ratio during the VAD synthesis process.

Keywords: SAXS, silica glass, VAD method, optical and structural homogeneity.
PACS: 01.30.Cc

INTRODUCTION

High quality synthetic silica glass (SiO_2) has been largely employed as lenses for photolithography equipments. For such application, a refractive index radial homogeneity less than 5 ppm and birefringence less than 2 nm/cm are of critical importance[2]. These optical properties are strictly related to the silica glass structure radial homogeneity, which can be achieved by controlling the processing parameters during the silica synthesis[3]. In this sense, the VAD (Vapor-phase Axial Deposition) flame aerosol method[4] is considered a promising technique to replace the CVD, the main current method used to produce high purity synthetic silica glass for such purpose. In the VAD process, silica nanoparticles are synthesized in an H_2-O_2 flame by the hydrolysis and oxidation reactions of $SiCl_4$ and axially deposited on a rotating target, forming a cylindrical-shaped porous boule. Afterwards, this boule is sintered at high temperature and transformed into a highly transparent glass. However, a challenge in the VAD process is to obtain structural and optical homogeneity along the radial direction, once the boule outer diameter region is alternately exposed to the flame due to the rotation movement, and consequently submitted to a cyclic heating and cooling process during the deposition stage. This process induces the formation of different nanostructures along the radial direction. In order to achieve an ultra-high

CP1092, *Synchrotron Radiation in Materials Science: 6th International Conference*, edited by R. Magalhaes-Paniago
© 2009 American Institute of Physics 978-0-7354-0625-4/09/$25.00

radial homogeneity material for optical components, sintered silica glass was produced through the VAD method by using different H_2/O_2 gases ratios and investigated by small angle X-ray scattering technique in correlation with its optical properties (refractive index homogeneity and birefringence).

METHODOLOGY

Sample preparation

Silica glass boules were produced by the VAD method[5] with H_2/O_2 ratios of 1.5, 2.0, 2.5, and 3.0 by maintaining the H_2 gas flux at 6000 sccm and changing the O_2 gas flux from 4000 to 2000 sccm. It was used a rotation speed of 25 rpm, $SiCl_4$ gas flux of 150 sccm, a five nozzle burner placed with 42° angle regarding the preform rotation axis and a distance from target of 57 mm. Afterwards, the silica boules were sintered at 1400 °C for two hours in He gas atmosphere.

SAXS measurements

The center and outer diameter regions of samples obtained by slicing sintered boules were characterized by small angle X-ray scattering (SAXS) at the Brazilian Synchrotron Light Laboratory (LNLS). D11A beamline was set at 7.47 keV (λ = 1.488 Å) by using Si(111) monochromator, and the scattered beam was detected by the image plate detector placed 2000 mm from the sample. The SAXS data were processed through the FIT2D[6] software.

Optical measurements

The refractive index radial homogeneity was measured with 10^{-6} accuracy by interferometry and optical spectrometry techniques. The birefringence was characterized by polarization spectrophotometry. For these measurements, 5.0 mm thick disks were prepared by slicing sintered boules and polished with optical finish.

RESULTS AND DISCUSSION

Fig. 1 shows the SAXS intensity curves for different H_2/O_2 ratios at centers and outer diameter regions. It was observed that, for all ratios used, the scattered intensities of silica boules center region are similar. In contrast, the SAXS scattered intensities of silica outer diameter region (edge) vary with the increase of the H_2/O_2 ratio and gradually superpose to the scattered intensity pattern of center region. This result indicates that a material with higher radial structural homogeneity is achieved for higher H_2/O_2 ratios.

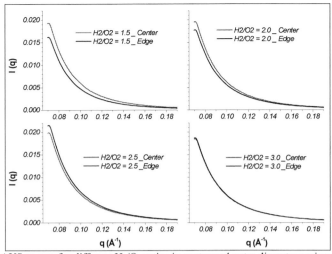

FIGURA 1. SAXS curves for different H_2/O_2 ratios in center and outer diameter regions of silica glass.

In accordance with this result, the Fig. 2 shows the effect of H_2/O_2 ratio on the size fluctuation in the electronic density (radius of gyration - R_g) obtained from the SAXS curves through the Guinier's approach in the range 0.069 $\text{Å}^{-1} \leq q \leq 0.082$ Å^{-1}. For the center regions, the R_g was estimated as ~28 nm, whereas the R_g composing the outer diameter regions are slightly reduced with the increase of H_2/O_2 ratio becoming approximately constant for $H_2/O_2 \geq 2.0$.

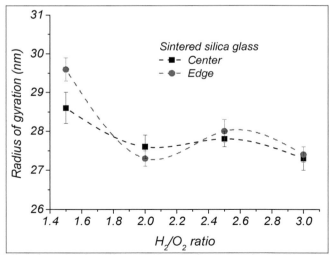

FIGURA 2. Radius of gyration for different H_2/O_2 ratios in center and outer diameter regions of silica glass boules.

In addition, from results hereinabove, it was verified that the SAXS intensities and radius of gyration of both regions presented a similar behavior when increasing the H_2/O_2 ratio, mainly for $H_2/O_2 \geq 2.0$, that means a more uniform structural homogeneity along radial direction of silica boule. In fact, for $H_2/O_2 = 3.0$, the difference of area under SAXS intensity curve between the center and outer diameter regions was $\Delta A = 2 \%$, whereas the greatest $\Delta A = 19 \%$ was obtained with $H_2/O_2 = 1.5$ (Fig. 3).

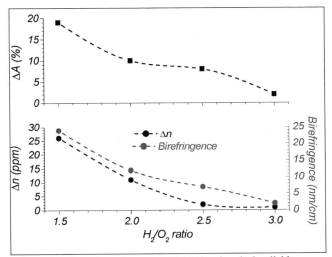

FIGURA 3. Effect of H_2/O_2 ratio on the structural (ΔA) and optical radial homogeneity (Δn and birefringence) of silica glass.

This result is in agreement with measurements of refractive index radial homogeneity and birefringence. Silica boule with low ΔA presented lower $\Delta n = 1 \times 10^{-6}$ and lower birefringence of 2 nm/cm. The maximum ΔA also corresponded to the maximum $\Delta n = 26 \times 10^{-6}$ and birefringence of 24 nm/cm (Fig. 3). Structural and optical radial homogeneity of silica synthesized by the VAD process is directly dependent on its bottom surface shape during the deposition process of silica nanoparticles. Different bottom surface shape and, consequently, its corresponding radial temperature distribution are obtained according to deposition parameters settings. For higher H_2/O_2 ratios, the boule surface shape becomes flatter (Fig. 4), as well as the radial variation of temperature is lower. This homogeneity in the temperature radial profile implies in higher radial homogeneity of silica nanostructure. In these cases, the size fluctuation in the electronic density and scattered intensities of center and outer diameter regions of sintered silica are similar.

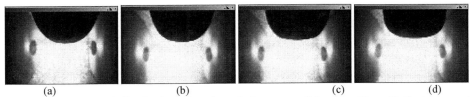

| (a) | (b) | (c) | (d) |

FIGURA 4. Progress of silica boule surface shape during nanoparticles deposition with the increase of H_2/O_2 ratio: (a) 1.5, (b) 2.0, (c) 2.5, and (d) 3.0.

CONCLUSIONS

The results have showed that there is a good correlation between the structural and optical radial homogeneity in sintered silica glass. Also, ultra-high radial homogeneity silica glass for optical components can be synthesized through VAD method controlling the H_2/O_2 ratio during the synthesis process where better results have been obtained with H_2/O_2 higher than 2.5.

ACKNOWLEDGMENTS

The authors would like to acknowledge FINEP/PADCT-III, Fapesp, CNPq, and CAPES for the financial support. Also, they acknowledge A. A. S. L. and C.C.N. for the experimental assistance and LNLS for providing the synchrotron radiation facilities.

REFERENCES

1. A. J. Ikushima et al., *J. Appl. Phys.* 2000, 88, 1201.
2. B. J. Bleaking, et al., U.S. Patent n. 2006/0137398 A1.
3. J. S. Santos, E. Ono, C. K. Suzuki, to be published in *J. Non-Cryst. Solids.*
4. T. Izawa, *IEEE J. Selected Topics in Quantum Electron.* 2000, 6, 1220.
5. J. S. Santos, E. Ono, C. K. Suzuki., *Rev. Sci. Instrum.* 2006, 77, 055106.
6. www.esrf.fr/computing/scientific/FIT2D.

Characterizing structural and vibrational properties of nanoparticles embedded in silica with XAS, SAXS and auxiliary techniques

Leandro L. Araujo[1]*, **Patrick Kluth[1]**, **Raquel Giulian[1]**, **David J. Sprouster[1]**, **Bernt Johannessen[2]**, **Garry J. Foran[2]**, **David J. Cookson[3]** and **Mark C. Ridgway[1]**

[1]*Department of Electronic Materials Engineering, Research School of Physical Sciences and Engineering, Australian National University, Canberra, ACT 0200, Australia (*lla109@rsphysse.anu.edu.au)*
[2]*Australian Nuclear Science and Technology Organisation, Menai, NSW 2234, Australia*
3 *Australian Synchrotron Research Program, Bldg 434, 9700 South Cass Avenue, Argonne IL 60439, USA*

Synchrotron-based techniques were combined with conventional analysis methods to probe in detail the structural and vibrational properties of nanoparticles grown in a silica matrix by ion implantation and thermal annealing, as well as the evolution of such properties as a function of nanoparticle size. This original approach was successfully applied for several elemental nanoparticles (Au, Co, Cu, Ge, Pt) and the outcomes for Ge are reported here, illustrating the power of this combined methodology. The thorough analysis of XANES, EXAFS, SAXS, TEM and Raman data for Ge nanoparticles with mean diameters between 4 and 9 nm revealed that the peculiar properties of embedded Ge nanoparticles, like the existence of amorphous Ge layers between the silica matrix and the crystalline nanoparticle core, are strongly dependent on particle size and mainly governed by the variation in the surface area-to-volume ratio. Such detailed information provides valuable input for the efficient planning of technological applications.

Introduction

Nanoparticles have been subject of extensive study in recent years [1]. Embedded nanoparticles, in particular, are promising candidates for improved light-emitting and charge-storing devices [2]. Synchrotron techniques are particularly well suited for the study of nanoscale systems, given their ensemble-probing and short-range sensitivity capabilities [3]. This work reports on combining synchrotron-based Extended X-ray Absorption Fine Structure (EXAFS), X-ray Absorption Near-Edge Structure (XANES) and Small-Angle X-ray Scattering (SAXS) to conventional Transmission Electron Microscopy (TEM) and Raman spectroscopy in order to carefully probe the growth and size-dependence of structural and vibrational properties of four silica-embedded Ge nanocrystal (NC) distributions produced by ion implantation and different annealing conditions.

Results and Discussion

The Ge NC size distributions were determined from SAXS measurements (Figure 1), yielding mean diameters of 4, 5, 6 and 9 nm. TEM images provided visual evidence of the formation of spherical particles with a crystalline core and support the results obtained from the SAXS analysis.

XANES spectra for the Ge NC samples showed no indication of Ge-O bonds, as it can be seen in Figure 2. Linear combination fits using bulk Ge standards revealed that the spectra of the Ge NCs are accurately reproduced as a combination of bulk-like amorphous and crystalline environments. The crystalline fraction decreased from 0.76 to 0.52 as the NC size decreases from 9 to 4 nm [4]. Raman data

further supported the conclusions derived from the SAXS and XANES results [4].

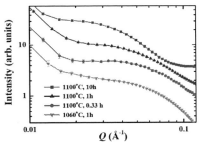

Figure 1. SAXS data obtained for the Ge NC samples after background subtraction using a blank SiO_2 standard. Annealing conditions leading to mean diameters of 4, 5, 6 and 9 nm are listed on the legend, from bottom to top, respectively. Spectra have been shifted vertically for clarity.

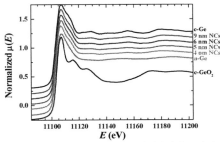

Figure 2. Normalized XANES spectra obtained for bulk standards and Ge NCs. Spectra have been shifted vertically for clarity.

CP1092, *Synchrotron Radiation in Materials Science: 6th International Conference*, edited by R. Magalhaes-Paniago
© 2009 American Institute of Physics 978-0-7354-0625-4/09/$25.00

EXAFS analysis (including multiple scattering effects) of the first three nearest neighbour (NN) shells showed that there is a decrease in coordination number and an increase in interatomic distance, structural disorder and asymmetry in the distribution of distances for the NCs as compared to bulk crystalline Ge [5]. EXAFS spectra measured at 15 K and corresponding Fourier transforms are shown in Figure 3. Temperature-dependent EXAFS measurements in the range 15 – 300 K were analyzed with a correlated Einstein model and thermodynamic perturbation theory [6]. Stiffer bond vibrations and reduced thermal expansion of interatomic distances were verified for the Ge NCs relative to bulk crystalline Ge. The difference between NCs and bulk increased as the NC size decreased for structural and vibrational properties [4].

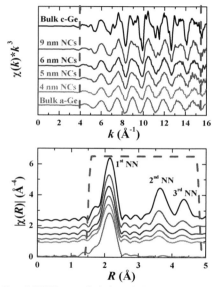

Figure 3. EXAFS spectra after background subtraction multiplied by k^3 (top) and corresponding Fourier transforms in non-phase-corrected radial space (bottom) for the Ge NC samples and bulk standards. The dashed lines indicate the region selected for Fourier transforming and fitting. Spectra have been shifted vertically for clarity in both panels.

Conclusion

Clear evidence of the formation of an amorphous-like Ge layer separating the amorphous silica matrix and the Ge crystalline core was found for embedded Ge NCs. This same phenomenon is predicted by very recent atomistic simulations of the interface structure of Si NCs embedded in amorphous silica [7]. Structural and vibrational parameters were shown to scale linearly with the inverse NC diameter, indicating that the surface area-to-volume ratio governs the properties of embedded Ge NCs [4]. Our results aid in explaining previously reported observations and contribute to the more efficient and rapid integration of Ge NCs in modern technologies.

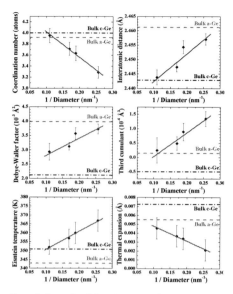

Figure 4. Structural and thermal parameters for the first nearest-neighbor shell obtained from EXAFS analysis of the Ge NCs samples, plotted as a function of the inverse NC diameter as obtained from SAXS measurements. Structural parameters were determined from the lowest-temperature measurements (15 K) and thermal parameters from measurements at eight different temperatures in the range 15 to 300 K. Symbols are values obtained for the NCs, full lines are linear fits to the symbols, dash-dot lines indicate the values obtained for the bulk c-Ge standard and dashed lines indicate the values obtained for the bulk a-Ge standard. Detailed discussion on these results can be found in references [4,5].

References

1. V. Rotello, D. J. Lockwood, *Nanoparticles: Building Blocks for Nanotechnology*, Springer-Verlag, New York, 2004.

2. J. Linnros *Nature Mater.* 2005, *4*, 117.

3. J. J. Rehr, R. C. Albers *Rev. Mod. Phys.* 2000, *72*, 621.

4. L. L. Araujo et al. *Phys. Rev. B* 2008, 78, 094112.

5. L. L. Araujo, G. J. Foran, M. C. Ridgway *J. Phys.: Condens. Matt.* 2008, 20, 165210.

6. L. L. Araujo et al. *Phys Rev. B* 2006, 74, 184102.

7. F. Djurabekova, K. Nordlund *Phys. Rev. B* 2008, 77, 115325.

Phospholipid/chitosan self-assemblies analyzed by SAXS and Light Scattering

Maria Lionzo, Omar Mertins, Adriana R. Pohlmann, Nádya P. da Silveira*

Instituto de Química - UFRGS, Av. Bento Gonçalves, 9500, Porto Alegre, Brazil nadya@iq.ufrgs.br

Abstract. Self-assemblies of phospholipids in an organic solvent (ethyl acetate) and their interaction with a cationic polysaccharide (chitosan) were appraised by scattering techniques. The investigations allowed following the formation of the self-assemblies and their dimensions as a function of components concentration over time.

Keywords: chitosan, phospholipids, SAXS, DLS.
PACS: 82.70.Uv, 83.85.Hf

INTRODUCTION

The knowledge about condensed organized/oriented systems, like membranes, has been largely improved by light scattering studies.[1,2] In this way, we have been scanning the chitosan (CH) influence on chitosomes, starting on the organogel stage until to the final vesicle formation.[3] Now, the goal is to perform a study in the systems named here pre-organogel self-assemblies, composed by phosphatidylcholine (PC) [0.6 to 60 mg/mL] and either water (W) or chitosan solution (1 mg/mL) (CH) [40 to 400 µL], dispersed in ethyl acetate (EA) [600 to 960 µL]. The experiments used Small Angle X-rays Scattering (SAXS) [LNLS Facilities, Campinas, Brazil] and Dynamic Light Scattering (LS) [Brookheaven Instruments, Porto Alegre, Brazil] techniques. The system kinetics was investigated over the 15 minutes after sample injection on the cells. The SAXS results was acquired using Fit 2D Program [ESRF, Grenoble, France] and DLS data was analyzed by GENDIST Program using the REPES algorithm.

RESULTS AND DISCUSSION

Small Angle X-rays Scattering results

The samples having higher amounts of PC [60 mg/mL] and either W or CH [400µL] showed anisotropy induced by shear during injection, which vanished throughout the analysis time.

CP1092, *Synchrotron Radiation in Materials Science: 6th International Conference*, edited by R. Magalhaes-Paniago

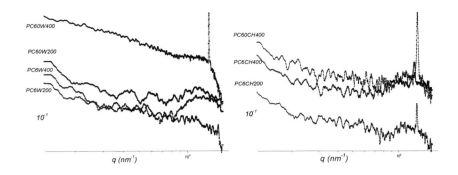

Figure 1 – SAXS profiles of different samples: PC/W(left); PC/CH (right).

Comparing the SAXS profiles of PC/W and PC/CH (Fig 1), it can be observed that the CH caused additional order, even in the samples with low CH content. The SAXS profiles are typical of micellar (L_2) and lamellar (L_α) mesophases.[4,5]

On the system composed by PC/W, a microgel (L_α) was observed for high W contents [400 µL]. When CH was present, a microgel was detected in samples having less water content. The bilayer width was near to 50 Å for all samples. After 15 min, the lamellar structure was retained only on the CH samples. The bilayer width suffers a small enlargement and mismatch over time. Comparing the Guinier region of the higher PC [60 mg/mL] and W or CH [400 µL], the PC/W combination gives lamellar and micellar structures, whereas PC/CH presented only lamellar ones.

Light Scattering results

Depolarized light scattering results showed anisotropy of PC/W composites when W content was in the highest content. Otherwise, to the PC/CH ones, small quantities of chitosan solution phase caused the same effect, amplifying the anisotropy. The micelles sizes were between 5.0 and 14 nm and the smaller aggregates ranged from 15 to 150 nm, whereas the bigger ones had between 150 and 600 nm. The microgels were larger than 600 nm. During the observation time, changes on the particles sizes, varying on different ways for each composition, were observed (Fig. 2). Typically, the PC/W distributions (left) raised small changes. Regarding PC/CH distribution curves, the progress of the micelles formation and the transition to bigger structures was observed (right).

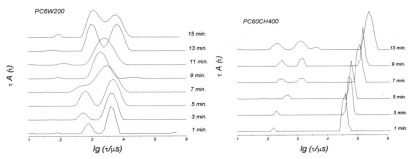

Figure 2 – Evolution of relaxation times obtained by LS: PC/W(left); PC/CH (right).

CONCLUSIONS

SAXS results put some light on the effects of CH at the PC organization on organic medium. The LS allowed to investigate the changes on the particles evolution during the analyses time, pointing out the CH capacity to aggregate the PC molecules in an arranged way. The results can be applied to improve the choice of the best composition to chitosomes preparation.

REFERENCES

1. Riske, K. A.; Amaral, L. Q.; Dobёreiner, H. G.; Lamy, M. T. *Biophys. J.* **86**, 3722 (2004).
2. Daillant, J. Comptes Rendus de l`Académie des Sciences – Serie IIB, **324**, 4, 239, 1997.
3. O. Mertins, Dissertação de Mestrado. Universidade Federal do Rio Grande do Sul, Brazil, 2004.
4. Weiss, T.; Narayanan, T.; Wolf, C.; Gradzielski, M.; Panine, P.; Finet, S.; Helsby, W. *Phys. Rev. Lett.* **94**, 038308 (2005).
5. Winter, R. *Biochim. Biophys. Acta.* **1595**, 160-184 (2002).

X-ray resonant diffraction of EuTe films and EuTe based superlattices

Beatriz Díaz Moreno*, Eduardo Abramof[a], Eduardo Granado[b], Carla Azimonte[b], Paulo H. Oliveira Rappl[a]

*Corresponding author: Laboratório Associado de Sensores e Materiais, Instituto Nacional de Pesquisas Espaciais, CP 515,12245-970, São José dos Campos – SP, Brazil. Tel. +55 12 3945-6578.
beatriz@las.inpe.br
[a] Laboratório Associado de Sensores e Materiais, Instituto Nacional de Pesquisas Espaciais, Brazil.
abramof@las.inpe.br, rappl@las.inpe.br
[b] Laboratório Nacional de Luz Síncrotron, Brazil. granado@lnls.br, carla@lnls.br

Abstract. In this work, we studied the resonant x-ray diffraction of single EuTe antiferromagnetic films and EuTe/PbTe(SnTe) superlattices. Below the Nèel temperature half order peaks appear, whose magnetic origin was proved by a polarization analysis. A resonant diffraction enhancement of almost three orders was found near the Eu L_{II} and L_{III} absorption edges. Unexpectedly high count rates of 40.000 cps were obtained for the 1.5 μm EuTe film. The magnetic diffraction signal from several EuTe/SnTe and EuTe/PbTe superlattices was also recorded. Magnetic and structural peaks were measured around T_N, yielding the transition temperature, the critical exponents, and proving that a lattice distortion accompanies the magnetic transition. In two EuTe/PbTe superlattices, a satellite structure of the magnetic peak was observed, demonstrating the existence of magnetic interlayer correlations, and the capability of x-ray resonant diffraction to detect such correlations in AFM systems, which to date was believed to be possible only by neutron diffraction.

Keywords: x-ray magnetic resonant diffraction, semiconductor superlattice, EuTe.
PACS: 61.05.cp, 68.65.Cd, 75.50.Pp, 75.75.+a

INTRODUCTION

The magnetic properties of europium chalcogenides EuX (X=O, S, Se, Te) have been extensively studied because of the strong localized moments which make them classical Heisenberg magnets [1, 2]. Bulk EuTe is a wide gap antiferromagnet with T_N=9.6K. The magnetic properties of EuTe films and EuTe/PbTe superlattices have already been studied by neutron diffraction. In this work we demonstrate the feasibility of resonant x-ray diffraction for the study of thin EuTe films and EuTe based superlattices. Common features of synchrotron radiation such as its brightness, collimation, high polarization and wide spectrum, make it ideal for the study of thin magnetic films.

CP1092, *Synchrotron Radiation in Materials Science: 6th International Conference,* edited by R. Magalhaes-Paniago
© 2009 American Institute of Physics 978-0-7354-0625-4/09/$25.00

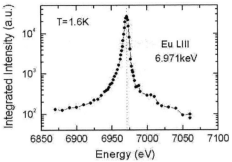

FIGURE 1. Strong resonances were observed near both Eu L_{II} and L_{III} absorption edges.

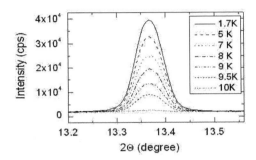

FIGURE 2 – EuTe magnetic peak (*hkl* ½ ½ ½) for different temperatures, measured at Eu L_{III} absorption edge.

X-ray magnetic resonant diffraction was used to investigate the properties of EuTe films of varying thicknesses and EuTe/PbTe(SnTe) superlattices. An enhancement of the diffracted intensity of more than two orders was found at Eu L_{II} and L_{III} absorption edges. The thermodynamic properties of the samples were studied recording the peak intensity for different temperatures near T_N. Two structural reflections were also measured, demonstrating that the magnetic transition was accompanied by a lattice distortion. The satellites of the magnetic reflection of two EuTe/PbTe superlattices proved the existence of interlayer correlations among the EuTe layers, and the suitability of x-ray resonant diffraction for the study of these systems.

REFERENCES

1. H. Kepa et al. *Phys. Rev. B* 2003, *68*, 024419.
2. J. Blinowski, P. Kacman *Phys. Rev. B* 2001, *64*, 045302.

Temperature-dependent EXAFS measurements of InP

C.S. Schnohr*[1], P. Kluth[1], L.L. Araujo[1], D.J. Sprouster[1], G.J. Foran[2], M.C. Ridgway[1]

[1]Department of Electronic Materials Engineering, Research School of Physical Sciences and Engineering, Australian National University, ACT 0200, Australia. Fax: +61 2 61250511, e-mail: css109@rsphysse.anu.edu.au
[2]Australian Nuclear Science and Technology Organisation, Menai, Australia

Abstract. The extended X-ray absorption fine structure (EXAFS) of crystalline InP was measured in the temperature range of $20 - 295$ K. Structural parameters were determined for the first, second and third nearest neighbor (NN) shells. The Debye-Waller factors increase as functions of both radial distance and temperature. The first NN Debye-Waller factor increases slowly with temperature whereas those for the second and third NN shell increase significantly. The influence of correlated motion on the vibrational behavior of the different shells is readily evidenced. Fitting an Einstein model to the first NN Debye-Waller factor yields an Einstein temperature $\theta_E = 394 \pm 8$ K, compared to a value of $\theta_E = 360 \pm 24$ K for GaAs. Debye temperatures reported for InP vary between 220 and 440 K depending on the temperature and method of determination.

INTRODUCTION

Temperature-dependent extended X-ray absorption fine structure (EXAFS) measurements yield unique insight into the thermal and vibrational properties of materials. Different to X-ray diffraction (XRD), for example, EXAFS is sensitive to the correlated motion of atomic pairs. Despite their technological importance, temperature-dependent EXAFS studies of semiconductors are primarily limited to monatomic systems, such as Ge, and a few compound materials, such as GaAs and CdSe. We now present the temperature dependent EXAFS study of crystalline InP over the temperature range of 20 to 295 K.

EXPERIMENTAL

The EXAFS of the In K-edge was measured in transmission mode at eight different temperatures ranging from 20 to 295 K. The measurements were performed

CP1092, *Synchrotron Radiation in Materials Science: 6th International Conference*, edited by R. Magalhaes-Paniago
© 2009 American Institute of Physics 978-0-7354-0625-4/09/$25.00

at beamline NW-10A of the Photon Factory, Japan. The EXAFS spectra were analyzed using the program IFEFFIT and the corresponding user interfaces ATHENA and ARTEMIS. The structural parameters were determined for the first three nearest neighbor (NN) shells.

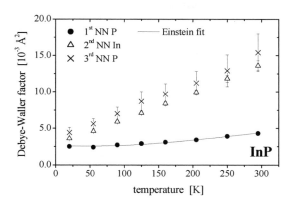

Figure 1: Debye-Waller factors for the first three nearest neighbor shells of crystalline InP as a function of temperature.

RESULTS

Figure 1 shows the Debye-Waller factor for the first NN P, the second NN In and the third NN P shells as a function of temperature. At a given temperature, the Debye-Waller factor increases with radial distance between absorber and scatterer. As a function of temperature, the first NN Debye-Waller factor increases only slightly whereas the second and third NN values increase significantly. A similar behavior has been observed for GaAs and is interpreted as a different extent to which correlation occurs in the atomic motion of the different shells [1]. Disorder can be accommodated by both bond stretching and bond bending and studies of ternary semiconductor alloys such as InGaP [2] reveal that the latter has the dominant role. Atomic vibrations perpendicular to the bond direction may thus be preferred over vibrations along the bond direction. The result is a Debye-Waller factor much reduced in comparison to that measured by XRD. For the second and third NN shell, correlated vibrational motion is significantly reduced.

Fitting an Einstein model to the first NN Debye-Waller factor yields an Einstein temperature of $\theta_E = 394 \pm 8$ K, compared to a value of $\theta_E = 360 \pm 24$ K for GaAs [1]. To our knowledge, no direct measurement of the Einstein temperature for InP has been reported. Debye temperatures published for InP vary between 220 and 440 K depending on the temperature [3] and method of determination [4].

REFERENCES

1. G. Dalba; D. Diop; P. Fornasini; F Rocca *J. Phys.. Condens. Matter* 1994, *6*, 3599.
2. C.S. Schnohr; L.L. Araujo; P. Kluth; D.J. Sprouster; G.J. Foran; M.C. Ridgway *Phys. Review B* 2008, *78*, 115201.
3. S. Adachi, *Properties of Group-IV, III-V and II-VI Semiconductors*, John Wiley & Sons, New York, 2005.
4. V.M.Glazov; A.S. Pashinkin; L.M. Pavlova *High Temperature* 2002, *40*, 369.

Effects of particle size and synthesis temperature on the structural properties of the Ni nanoparticles: Insights about the formation of the fcc-Ni structure

Edvaldo Alves de Souza*,a, Hebert Winnischofer^b, Paula Haddad^a, Tulio C. R. Costa^{a,c}, Daniela Zanchet^a

^a Brazilian Synchrotron Light Laboratory, Chemical Synthesis Laboratory, 13083-970 Campinas, SP, Brazil
^b University of Paraná State, 81531-990, Curitiba, PR, Brazil
^c University of Campinas State, Campinas, São Paulo, Brazil
*edvaldo.alves.2002@gmail.com

Abstract. Nickel nanoparticles (NPs) have been studied due to their superparamagnetic features and potential applications in magnetic devices. Nickel NPs are also interesting because they can be synthesized in three different structures, amorphous, hcp-Ni and fcc-Ni. This work presents the structural studies of Nickel NPs. The results are based on the analysis of the oxidation state and the structural local order around Ni atoms of NPs synthesized at different particle sizes and synthesis temperatures.

Keywords: Nanoparticles, colloidal Synthesis, Structure, XANES, EXAFS, XRD

PACS: 81.07.-b; 81.16.Be; 81.05.Bx; 87.64.kd; 87.64.Ee;

INTRODUCTION

The possibility of synthesizing Nickel NPs in three different structures and the fact of hcp-Ni is not found in nature it gives to these NPs a great deal of attention [1,2]. Several syntheses about the three different structures are described in literature and they show that controlling the structure demand on rigid control of the reaction parameters [1,3]. In these papers, the research groups have demonstrated that changing the temperature is one way to control the structures of the Nickel NPs. Through the increase of the temperature during the synthesis reaction they got altering fcc-Ni to hcp-Ni. The growth of the particle is also observed in this change. This work presents the structural studies of Ni NPs by X-ray Absorption Spectroscopy (XAS), X-Ray Diffraction (XRD) and Transmission Electron Microscopy (TEM). The results are based on analysis of the structure of Nickel NPs synthesized in different synthesis temperatures and particle size.

CP1092, *Synchrotron Radiation in Materials Science: 6th International Conference*, edited by R. Magalhaes-Paniago
© 2009 American Institute of Physics 978-0-7354-0625-4/09/$25.00

EXPERIMENTAL

Nickel NPs were synthesized with sizes ranging from 4 to 16 nm by synthesis based on *n*-trioctylamine and triocttyl- phosphine as stabilizing agent; $Ni(CH_3COO)_2$ $4H_2O$ and $Ni(acac)_2$ as precursors reagents; and phenylether and diphenylhter as solvent. Docecanodiol was used as surfactant. XAS data were collected at the Ni K-edge at the D04B – XAS/LNLS beamline from powder samples at 20 and 300 K. TEM images were obtained in a JEOL JEM-3010 microscope (300kV, 1.7 Å point resolution) at LME/LNLS. XRD analyses were carried out on XRD1/LNLS beam line (7.0026 KeV).

RESULTS

Samples were synthesized to study the evolution from a-Ni to fcc-Ni structures. The figure 1 presents XRD measurements to amorphous (~12 nm) and crystalline (~5nm) samples.

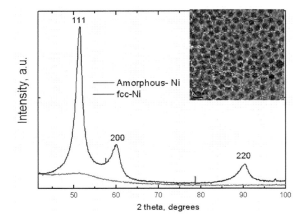

FIGURE 1. XRD of the a-Ni and fcc-Ni structures. Inside the a-Ni TEM image (scale = 20 nm).

The only one difference in their synthesis is the temperature of addition of the surfactant. Inside the figure 1 there is another with an image of the a-Ni NPs. The size effect on the crystallinity was observed in NPs synthesized in similar synthesis, but different ratio among the reagents. Two of them were annealed at 230°C after synthesis to modify their structure. The figure 2 presents XANES analysis. It shows the separation of the oxidation state between the samples and Ni-bulk. The higher particle size and temperature of synthesis are, the closer the oxidation state is to the metal nickel.

136

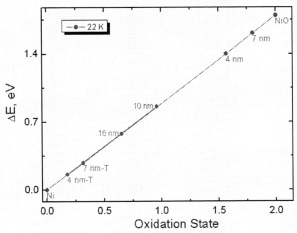

FIGURE 2. Results of XANES analyses

The Analysis EXAFS (tab. 1) supports the analysis XANES and it shows that the higher particle size and synthesis temperature are, the closer the samples are of the Ni structure.

Table1. EXAFS analyses around Ni atoms at 22K.

NPs Size	Coordination number	
	Ni	O
4nm	*0.7*	*2.9*
4 nm – T	6.7	1.7
7 nm	*0.9*	*3.1*
7 nm –T	6.9	1.6
10 nm	*6.0*	*2.3*

CONCLUSIONS

In XAS, XRD and TEM analyses were possible to observe that the increase of the synthesis temperature and NPs size modifies the bond of the nickel atom in Nickel NPs structure.

REFERENCES

1. C. N. Chinnasamy; B. Jeyadevan; K. Shinoda; K. Tohji, A. Narayanasamy, K. Sato; S. Hisano J. Appl. Phys. 2005, 97, 10J309.
2. H. Liu; X. Ge; Y. Zhu; X. Xu; Z. Zhang; M. Zhang. Materials Letters, 2000, 46, 205.
3. V Tzitzios; G Basina; M Gjoka; V Alexandrakis; V Georgakilas; D Niarchos; N Boukos; D Petridis. Nanotechnology, 2006, 17, 3750.

Quantum size effect as evidenced by small-angle X-ray scattering of In_2O_3 nanoparticles

E. C. C. Souza, J. F. Q. Rey, E. N. S. Muccillo[*]

Centro de Ciência e Tecnologia de Materiais, Instituto de Pesquisas Energéticas e Nucleares, R. do Matão, Trav. R, 400, Cidade Universitária, S. Paulo, SP, 05508-000, Brazil, eccsouza@gmail.com, jfqrey@gmail.com, enavarro@usp.br (E.N.S.Muccillo).

Abstract. Indium oxide nanoparticles were synthesized by a surfactant-free room-temperature soft chemistry route. The medium particle size of the thermally treated gel was evaluated by X-ray diffraction experiments, nitrogen adsorption measurements, transmission electron microscopy observations and small-angle X-ray scattering using synchrotron radiation. The main results show the single-crystalline nature of the prepared nanoparticles with 8 nm in diameter. The photoluminescence emission spectrum at room-temperature shows a broad peak with onset at, approximately, 315 nm as a result of quantum size effect produced by a small population of nanoparticles with average size of about 2.8 nm as revealed by small-angle X-ray scattering.

Keywords: SAXS, indium oxide, quantum size effect.
PACS: 61.05.cf; 78.55.Hx; 81.07.Bc

INTRODUCTION

Indium oxide, a wide band gap (about 3.6 eV) transparent conductor, is of great interest for many device applications due to its unusual combination of high transparency in the visible region and high electrical conductivity.

In this work, In_2O_3 nanoparticles were synthesized by a surfactant-free room-temperature soft chemistry route. Structural and microstructural properties were evaluated by several techniques.

EXPERIMENTAL

Nanosized indium oxide was synthesized by homogeneous precipitation at room-temperature. The colloidal dispersion was dried and thermally treated at 400°C for 2 h. The specific surface area was determined from nitrogen adsorption measurements. The average value of the crystallite size was estimated from X-ray diffraction patterns. The morphology of powder particles was observed by transmission electron microscopy. Photoluminescence emission spectra were recorded at room-temperature. Small-angle X-ray scattering measurements were carried out at

CP1092, Synchrotron Radiation in Materials Science: 6th International Conference, edited by R. Magalhaes-Paniago
© 2009 American Institute of Physics 978-0-7354-0625-4/09/$25.00

the Brazilian Synchrotron Light Laboratory. Experimental data were fitted using the GNOM software [2].

RESULTS AND DISCUSSION

The particle size diameter calculated from specific surface area assuming a spherical shape for the particles resulted in 7.8 nm. This value is in close agreement with the crystallite size (about 8 nm) estimated for the most intense (222) reflection of the cubic bixbyite-type structure of In_2O_3.

Transmission electron microscopy observations show that indium oxide nanoparticles are spherical in shape with a narrow distribution of size. The primary particle size estimated is 8 nm in diameter.

The room-temperature photoluminescence spectrum of indium oxide nanoparticles shows a broad emission peak with onset at ~ 315 nm, which is blue-shifted compared to that of commercial In_2O_3.
Small-angle X-ray scattering results were fitted assuming a polydisperse system of spherical particles [3]. Figure 1 shows the resulting distribution curve.

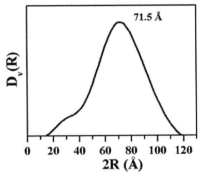

Figure 1 – Volumetric size distribution curve calculated from fitted experimental SAXS data.

The size distribution curve consists of two populations of particle sizes. The smallest one is centered at ~ 2.8 nm giving a direct evidence of a quantum size effect in In_2O_3 nanoparticles, which in turn, is responsible for the photoluminescence emission at room-temperature.

CONCLUSIONS

A quantum size effect was verified by small-angle X-ray diffraction in In_2O_3 nanoparticles. This method proved to be suitable for a detailed study of very fine particulate materials.

REFERENCES

1. A. V. Semenyuk, D. I. Svergun *J. Appl. Cryst.* 1997, *24*, 537.
2. G. Beaucage; H. K. Kammler; S. E. Pratsinis *J. Appl. Cryst.* 2004, *37*, 523.

SAXS investigation of the structure of the pore walls in thermosensitive macroporous hydrogels

Françoise Ehrburger-Dolle[a], Isabelle Morfin[a], Françoise Bley[b], Maria Rosa Aguilar[c], Alberto Gallardo[c], Paloma Perez[c], Julio San Roman[c], Fatima Plieva[d,e], Igor Yu. Galaev[e], Bo Mattiasson[e], Sergey Mikhalovsky[f]

[a]Laboratoire de Spectrométrie Physique, UMR5588 CNRS-UJF, 38402 Saint-Martin d'Hères, France;
[b]SIMaP UMR5266 CNRS-UJF-INPG, 38402 Saint-Martin d'Hères, France;
[c]Instituto de Ciencia y Tecnologia de Polimeros, CSIC, 28006 Madrid, Spain;
[d]Protista Biotechnology AB, Ideon, SE-22370 Lund, Sweden; [e]Department of Biotechnology, Center for Chemistry and Chemical Engineering, Lund University,SE-22100 Lund, Sweden;
[f]School of Pharmacy &Biomolecular Sciences, University of Brighton, Brighton BN2 4GJ, UK;

Abstract. The meso- and nano-structure of thermosensitive macroporous polymers ("cryogels") is investigated by SAXS, showing that the nanostructure of the sample is related to swelling.

Keywords: Macroporous hydogels, cryogels, pNIPA, SAXS
PACS: 61.25.hp; 78.70.Ck; 82.70.Gg

INTRODUCTION

Intelligent polymeric materials, which exhibit response to external stimuli, such as temperature, have gathered a great interest in recent years. Poly(N-isopropylacrylamide) (pNIPA) hydrogels are well-known to exhibit a volume transition at a critical temperature (LCST) T_c close to 33 °C in aqueous media. Below T_c, pNIPA hydrogels are swollen, hydrated and hydrophilic. Above T_c, the gels shrink due to the distortion of the hydrophilic/hydrophobic balance in the network structure. One of the important characteristics of pNIPA hydrogels is the reversibility of shrinking-swelling cycle in response to changes of environmental conditions. However, the rate of response to external temperature changes of pNIPA hydrogels is low due to the formation of a dense "skin layer" of the shrunken gel which prevents the mass-transport of water out of the shrinking gel. The slow response restricts the application of pNIPA hydrogels.

A way to accelerate the response of pNIPA gels consists in the synthesis of a macroporous structure. The macropores serve as channels that facilitate convective transport of liquid released during the shrinkage of the gel. An efficient way to form porous structures is to use the crystals of a frozen solvent as a porogen avoiding the introduction of new chemicals in the system. Gels obtained at temperatures below the melting temperature of the solvent are called cryogels. At these temperatures most of the solvent is frozen, while the dissolved substances are concentrated in small non-frozen regions, so called "liquid microphase". As the volume of the non-frozen liquid microphase is much less than that of the solid phase, the local monomer concentration is much higher than the monomer concentration in the initial reaction mixture[1]. The gel formation occurs in this liquid microphase and the crystals of frozen solvent perform like porogen. After melting the ice crystals, a system of large interconnected macropores is formed[2].

The aim of the SAXS measurements reported here was to investigate the meso- and nano-structure of the macropore walls in cryogels and in gels obtained in the same chemical conditions. All samples were measured in the dry and the wet state, below and above T_c.

EXPERIMENTAL

Samples

The samples investigated are pNIPA cryogels[3] cross-linked with two different bis-acrylic compounds:
- *N,N´*-methylenebisacrylamide (MBAAm) in water
- dimethacrylate-tyrosine-lysine-tyrosine (DMTLT) in water or in an aqueous dioxane solution.
Classical gels were prepared in the same chemical conditions, at room temperature, for comparison.

SAXS measurements

SAXS measurements were performed at ESRF on the French CRG beamline D2AM. The incident energy was set to 15.193 keV ($\lambda = 0.77$ Å). The detector, an indirect illumination CCD camera (Princeton Instruments), with pixel size equal to 50 μm was located at distances of 206.4 and 35.1 cm from the sample. These configurations provided data for wave vectors q ranging between 5×10^{-2} and 10 nm^{-1}. Data obtained from the detector were corrected by taking into account the flat field and the dark current. The swollen samples were placed in stainless steel holders closed by two mica windows 1 mm apart. For these samples, scattering of the same thickness of pure water was subtracted from the total intensity. No mica windows were used for the dry samples. The CCD images were processed by means of the software *bm2img* available on the beamline.

RESULTS AND DISCUSSION

Figure 1a compares the SAXS curves obtained in the high-q domain for the pNIPA cryogel and the gel cross-linked with DMTLT in an aqueous dioxane solution (sample d-D). In the dry state, the two samples show a broad peak located at 5.49 and 5.67 nm^{-1} for the gel and the cryogel, respectively. The corresponding characteristic length, d, in the real space, can be obtained, as a first approximation, by mean of the Bragg relation: $d = 2\pi/q$ yielding 1.14 and 1.11 nm for the gel and the cryogel, respectively. It follows that the nano-structure of the dry cryogel is similar to that of the corresponding classical gel. This distance d is nearly twice the length of the side groups. Thus, it may be assumed that d is a mean distance between main chains when interactions between neighbour side-groups is no longer screened by water molecules. In the wet state, however, the gel still displays this peak, yet attenuated, while this peak nearly vanishes in the wet cryogel. Vanishing of the peak in the swollen cryogels at temperatures below T_c may indicate complete swelling. This result suggests that the classical gel may not be fully swollen. Interestingly, the swelling ratio of the cryogel is larger than for the gel synthesised at room temperature in the same chemical conditions.

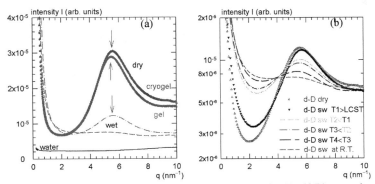

FIGURE 1a. Comparison between the SAXS curves of DMTLT/pNIPA(d-D) cryogel and gel (obtained by the classical method) in dried and swollen state.
FIGURE 1b. Comparison between the SAXS curves obtained for DMTLT/pNIPA(d-D) cryogel during cooling down in water from a temperature above T_c and for the dry cryogel.

In order to investigate the structure of a cryogel above the T_c, the sample DMTLT/pNIPA (d-D), swollen in water was heated at 60°C and cooled down to room temperature (R.T.). Figure 1b shows that the high-q SAXS curves are nearly identical for the dry cryogel and the swollen cryogel at a temperature above the critical temperature T_c corresponding to the volume phase transition (LCST). It follows that the nanostructure is probably the same after deswelling by evaporation of water and by heating above T_c.

ACKNOWLEDGMENTS

This work was financially supported by Protista International AB (Bjuv, Sweden), The Swedish Foundation for Strategic Research, The Swedish Foundation for International Cooperation in Research and Higher education (STINT, IG2003-2089), The Swedish Institute (Visby Program, projects 2886/2002 and 01211/2004), Royal Swedish Academy of Sciences. Financial support from the grant MAT 2004-01654 from the CICYT and the NoE. EXPERTISSUES from the EC is acknowledged. The authors are grateful to the ESRF, Grenoble, for access to the French CRG beamline D2AM (proposal No. 0201702) and they acknowledge the help of its technical staff, J.F. Berar, N. Boudet, B. Caillot, S. Arnaud.

REFERENCES

1. V.I. Lozinsky VI. *Russ. Chem. Rev.* 2002, *71,* 489.
2. F.M. Plieva, M. Karlsson, M.R. Aguilar, D. Gomez, S. Mikhalovsky, I.Y. Galaev, *Soft Matter* 2005, *1*, 303.
3. P. Perez, F. Plieva, A. Gallardo, J. San Roman, M.R. Aguilar, I. Morfin, F. Ehrburger-Dolle, F. Bley, S. Mikhalovsky, I.Y. Galaev, B. Mattiasson, *Biomacromol.* 2008, *9*, 66.

Study of the Crystalline Morphology Evolution of PET and PET/PC Blends by Time-resolved Synchrotron Small Angle X-ray Scattering (SAXS) and DSC

Irineu Barbosa Jr[a], Nelson M. Larocca[a], Tomas S. Plivelic[b], Iris L. Torriani[b], Elias Hage Jr[a], Gerson L. Mantovani[c]

[a]Dep. de Engenharia de Materiais, Universidade Federal de São Carlos, São Carlos, SP, Brazil
[b]Laboratório Nacional de Luz Síncrotron, Campinas, SP, Brazil
[c]Centro de Engenharia, Modelagem e Ciências Sociais Aplicadas, Universidade Federal do ABC, 09090-400 Santo André, SP, Brazil

Abstract. Isothermal melt crystallization of poly(ethylene terephthalate) (PET) and PET/PC (polycarbonate) blend, with and without a transesterification catalyst, was studied by time-resolved small-angle X-ray scattering (SAXS) and differential scanning calorimetry (DSC) in order to achieve the variation of the morphological parameters throughout the whole crystallization time. For neat PET, the catalyst promotes a decrease of the crystal lamellar thickness but for the blend no variations were observed. The effect of incorporation of catalyst in crystallization kinetics was very distinct in PET pure and the blend: in the former the catalyst leads to an increase of this kinetics while for the latter it was observed a decreasing.

Keywords: Polymer blends, PET/PC blends, crystalline morphology, SAXS, DSC.
PACS: 70.20Rv

INTRODUCTION

Binary blends of poly(ethylene terephthalate) (PET) and polycarbonate (PC) are technologically attractive, since they combine the good engineering properties of PC with that of PET. As the properties of blends are usually very sensible to the crystalline morphology of the crystallizable polymer, it is fundamental to understand how the amorphous PC influences the process of the crystallization of PET.

Polyesters blends are able to promote transesterefication reactions during any melt blending process, mainly due to high temperature and high shear involved during the mixing[1-5]. Transesterification reactions may occur due to different types of reactions such as hydrolytic and thermal degradations, alcoholysis and acidolysis. As a result of all possible transesterification reactions, several molecular changes in the polyester blend may occur such as copolymerization and formation of chain segments with different molecular weights. Any molecular modification may lead to changes in the crystallization rates and in the resulting crystallinity degree of any of the polyester component in those blends[6,7].

CP1092, Synchrotron Radiation in Materials Science: 6th International Conference, edited by R. Magalhaes-Paniago
© 2009 American Institute of Physics 978-0-7354-0625-4/09/$25.00

PET/PC blends are immiscible even in the molten state over a wide range of compositions, but the interaction between PET and PC can be improved through transesterifications reactions, which leads to the formation of copolymers of PET-PC that enhance the blend miscibility. The use of transesterification catalysts increase these reaction rates in a large extent.

In this work we investigated the effects of the incorporation of a transesterefication catalyst on the crystalline morphology evolution during an isothermal crystallization of pure PET and PET/PC blend.

EXPERIMENTAL

The bisphenol-A PC and PET used were commercial materials supplied by GE Plastics South America and Rhodia (Brazil) under trade names Lexan 141R (I.V. of 0.45 dL.g^{-1}) and S80 (I.V. of 0.8 dL.g^{-1}), respectively. The catalyst, tetrakis(2-ethylhexyl)titanate was supplied by DuPont.

PET/PC blends (50/50 wt/wt) were prepared by melt mixing in a co-rotating twin-screw extruder (Werner-Pfleiderer model ZSK-30) at 275 °C and 100 rpm. Prior to melt blending or injection molding all materials were dried in a vacuum oven for 24 h at 100 °C. It was produced without and with addition of 250 ppm tetrakis(2-ethylhexyl)titanate as a catalyst. Catalyst addition levels were calculated based on the percentage of titanium in catalyst. All blend components were thoroughly mixed prior to extrusion. Samples for the SAXS and DSC measurements were prepared by injection molding process at 280 °C, with a mold temperature of 30 °C.

SAXS measurements were performed at the small angle scattering workstation (D11A) at National Synchrotron Light Laboratory - LNLS, Campinas, Brazil, using a linear position sensitive detector. A Linkam DSC (model THM 600) of single-pan design was used for the samples temperature control for the isothermal crystallization experiments. The samples were cut from the molded samples and encapsulated in DSC pans fitted with mica windows. In the experiments, the samples were initially equilibrated at 270 °C (above the melt temperature of PET) for 5 minutes and after that the temperature was jumped in a high cooling rate to the crystallization temperature at 210 °C.

RESULTS AND DISCUSSION

Neat PET : SAXS results show that catalyst promotes a decrease of the crystal lamellar thickness (*lc*) of PET, but the amorphous lamellar thickness (*la*) is not altered (FIG. 1-a). The decrease of '*lc*' by the incorporation of catalyst can possibly be explained by the PET transesterefication promoted by this component. This process alter the PET chains structure and thus may alter the stacking order of the chains.

DSC thermograms (FIG. 1-b) show that catalyst promotes a large increase of the crystallization kinetics. A possible explanation for the increase of the crystallization kinetics by the incorporation of catalyst is that this component can act as a nucleating agent.

Blend: SAXS results show that catalyst does not promotes a clear alteration of '*lc*' or '*la*' of PET/PC blend in contrast with the effect in pure PET (FIG.2-a). This may occur because it is likely that copolymers formed by transesterefication are pulled out from the PET crystals during the crystallization.

DSC results (FIG. 2-b) show that, in contrast with PET, catalyst induces a decrease of the crystallization kinetics of the PET in the PET/PC blend. A possible explanation for the decreasing is as follows: the copolymers formed by the transesterification reactions have a strong interaction with the melt PET phase. This difficult the crystallization of this phase, since the copolymers have to be expulsed of this phase in order to allow the crystal formation.

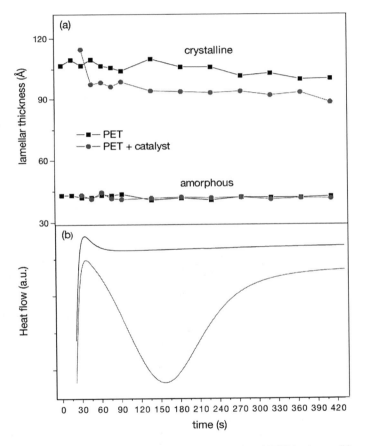

FIGURE 1. Effect of catalyst on neat PET; SAXS results (a) and DSC isotherms (b) *vs.* time of isothermal crystallization.

147

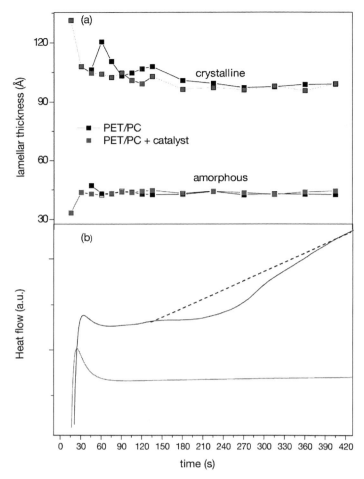

FIGURE 2. Effect of catalyst on PET/PC blend; SAXS results (a) and DSC isotherms (b) vs. time of isothermal crystallization

CONCLUSIONS

The incorporation of the catalyst in PET decrease its crystal lamellar thickness and increase the crystallization kinetics. For the PET/PC blend with the catalyst, the crystal lamellar thickness does not change significantly in comparison with the neat blend, but a large decrease of crystallization kinetics is observed.

ACKNOWLEDGMENTS

This work has been supported by the Brazilian Synchrotron Light Laboratory (LNLS) under the proposal D11A–SAXS1–4820; **FAPESP** (Proj. PIPE 03/07915-2), **CNPq** (Proc. Nº 481853/2007-3). We also thank to GE Plastics, Rhodia-Ster and Du-Pont Brazil for the donation of the polymers and catalyst.

REFERENCES

1. L. B. Canto, G. L. Mantovani, J. A. Covas et al., *Journal of Applied Polymer Science* **104**, 102 (2007).
2. G. L. Mantovani, L. B. Canto, E. Hage et al., *Macromolecular Symposia* **176**, 167 (2001).
3. G. L. Mantovani, L. A. Pessan, E. Hage et al., *6th Brazilian Polymer Conference,* Gramado, Brazil, (2001).
4. G. L. Mantovani, T. S. Plivelic, I. L. Torriani et al., *Activity Report LNLS 2001*, 156 (2002).
5. G. L. Mantovani, C. A. Perez, I. B. Barbosa Jr et al., *Activity Report LNLS 2003*, 179 (2004).
6. E. Hage, L. A. S. Ferreira, S. Manrich et al., *J. Appl. Polym. Sci.* **71**, 423 (1999).
7. J-C Ho and K-H Wei, *Polymer* **40**, 717 (1999).

Phase transition in $Ba_2In_2O_5$ studied by *in situ* high temperature X-ray diffraction using synchrotron radiation

J. F. Q. Rey[1,2*], F. F. Ferreira[3], E. N. S. Muccillo[1]

[1]*Instituto de Pesquisas Energéticas e Nucleares, R. do Matão, Trav. R, 400 cidade Universitária, S. Paulo, SP, 05508-000, Brazil, jfqrey@gmail.com (J.F.Q.Rey), enavarro@usp.br (E.N.S.Muccillo) ,* [2]*Universidade Federal do ABC,* [3]*Laboratório Nacional de Luz Sincrotron, furlan@lnls.br*

Abstract. The order-disorder phase transition in $Ba_2In_2O_5$ high-temperature ionic conductor was systematically studied by *in situ* high-temperature X-ray diffraction using synchrotron radiation and electrical conductivity. Pure barium indate was prepared by solid state reactions at 1300°C. The room-temperature structural characterization showed a high degree of phase homogeneity in the prepared material. The reduction of the order-disorder phase transition temperature was verified by electrical conductivity and high-temperature X-ray diffraction. The observed features were explained based on Fourier-transform infrared spectroscopy results that revealed the presence of hydroxyl species in the crystal lattice. The increase of the intensity of few diffraction peaks near the phase transition temperature suggests the formation of a superstructure before the orthorhombic-to-tetragonal phase transition.

Keywords: X ray diffraction, rietveld, barium indate.
PACS: 61.05.cp, 61.66.Fn

$Ba_2In_2O_5$ mixed oxide has received great attention due to its interesting electrical properties. In the low-temperature range (up to ~ 400°C) this mixed oxide exhibits proton conduction, and for increasing temperatures, mixed conduction was reported with predominance of ionic conduction above 700°C[1]. Around 925°C the magnitude of the electrical conductivity increases abruptly due to an order-disorder phase transition[2]. These changes in the conduction mechanism are in some way related to the crystalline structure of $Ba_2In_2O_5$.

EXPERIMENTAL

Pure $Ba_2In_2O_5$ was prepared by solid state reactions between the cation nitrates. The sintering of pellets was carried out at 1300°C for 10 h. Phase characterization was done by X-ray diffraction. Phase transition studies were accomplished by *ac* electrical conductivity and *in situ* high-temperature X-ray diffraction using the XPD D10B powder diffraction beamline of the Brazilian Synchrotron Light Laboratory. A special setup was used, which consists of a furnace attached to an automated image plate detection system[3]. All diffraction patterns were fitted through Rietveld refinement using GSAS program.

CP1092, *Synchrotron Radiation in Materials Science: 6th International Conference*, edited by R. Magalhaes-Paniago
© 2009 American Institute of Physics 978-0-7354-0625-4/09/$25.00

RESULTS AND DISCUSSION

Figure 1 shows X-ray diffraction patterns in the 45° to 65° 2θ range collected during heating of the sample up to 950°C. It is worth noting that at a temperature as low as 825°C the order-disorder phase transition has already started and at 882°C it has been finished, in agreement with electrical conductivity results.

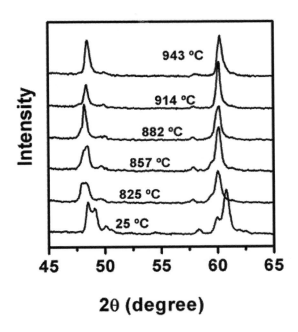

Figure 1 – High-temperature X-ray diffraction patterns of $Ba_2In_2O_5$.

CONCLUSIONS

A reduction of the phase transition temperature by about 50 °C, when compared to materials prepared by the conventional solid state mixture of starting oxides/carbonates was obtained, due to hydroxyls incorporated into the crystal lattice of $Ba_2In_2O_5$.

REFERENCES

1. J. B. Goodenough; J. E. Ruiz-Dias; Y. S. Zhen *Solid State Ionics* 1990, *44*, 21.

2. K. R. Kendall; C. Navas; J. K. Thomas; H.-C. zur Loye *Solid State Ionics* 1995, *82*, 215.
3. F. F. Ferreira; E. Granado; W. Carvalho Jr; S. W. Kycia; D. Bruno; R. Droppa Jr *J. Synchrotron Rad.* 2006, *13*, 46.

Study Of Phase Transition In Nanostructured ZrO$_2$-CeO$_2$ Solid Solutions By Synchrotron Radiation

L.M. Acuña[1], D.G. Lamas[1], R.O. Fuentes[1] and M.C.A. Fantini[2]

(1) CINSO (Centro de Investigaciones en Sólidos), CITEFA-CONICET, J.B. de La Salle 4397 (1603) Villa Martelli, Pcia. de Buenos Aires, Argentina, e-mail: lacuna@citefa.gov.ar; rfuentes@citefa.gov.ar; dlamas@citefa.gov.ar
(2) Instituto de Física, Universidade de São Paulo, São Paulo, Brasil, mail: mfantini@if.usp.br

Abstract. In this work we studied the tetragonal to cubic (t-c) phase transition as function of temperature in compositionally homogeneous ZrO$_2$-CeO$_2$ powders by synchrotron radiation X-ray diffraction (SR-XRD). Transitions are correlated with changes in the local order of the second coordination shell of Zr atom, studied by EXAFS.

Keywords: Nanocrystals, zirconia, EXAFS, HT-XRD.
PACS: 61.46.Hk

INTRODUCTION

Compositionally homogeneous ZrO$_2$-CeO$_2$ solid solutions exhibit 3 tetragonal forms ($P4_2/nmc$ space group). The stable tetragonal form is called the t-form and is restricted to the solubility limit predicted by the equilibrium phase diagram. The t'-form has an expanded solubility but is unstable against the mixture of t-form and cubic phase. Finally, the t"-form has an axial ratio c/a of unity but with the oxygen atoms displaced along the c axis from their ideal sites of the cubic phase (8c sites of the $Fm3m$ space group). If CeO$_2$ content is further increased, the cubic phase is retained. In previous works carried out at LNLS, we investigated the crystal structure and the local order at room temperature of compositionally homogenous ZrO$_2$-CeO$_2$ nanopowders synthesized by gel-combustion routes. By means of XPD, we determined the crystal structure of the solid solutions as a function of CeO$_2$ content and found that the tetragonal/cubic boundary is located at 85 mol% CeO$_2$ [1]. In addition, EXAFS study showed that this tetragonal-cubic transition is associated to a symmetry change in the Zr-O coordination sphere, while the Ce-O one has a cubic symmetry in the whole compositional range [2].

EXPERIMENTAL

ZrO$_2$-50 and 65 mol% CeO$_2$ powders were synthesized by citrate-complexation (CC) and gel-combustion (GC) methods [1,3]. High temperature X-ray

CP1092, *Synchrotron Radiation in Materials Science: 6th International Conference*, edited by R. Magalhaes-Paniago
© 2009 American Institute of Physics 978-0-7354-0625-4/09/$25.00

diffraction (HT-XRD) and HT-EXAFS measurements were carried out at the LNLS (Campinas, Brazil).

RESULTS AND DISCUSSION

Crystallite size (D) was determined from XRD patterns using the Scherrer formula. Results are shown in Table 1. The evolution of the (112) reflection with temperature was followed for all compositions, in order to discriminate between tetragonal and cubic phases.

TABLE 1. Transition Temperature (T_c) and Crystallite Sizes (D) for the Different Powders. *Extrapolated; **Estimated

Composition (mol% CeO$_2$)	Method	D (nm)	Transition	T_C (°C)
50	CC	10	t'→c	≈1000*
	GC	29	t'→c	----
65	CC	8	t"→c	≈650**
	GC	33	t'→t"	700
			t"→c	≈1090*

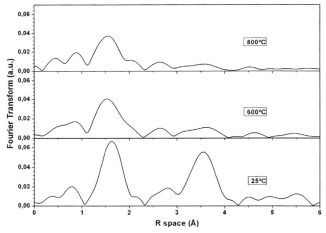

FIGURE 1: Fourier Transform of the EXAFS signal at different temperatures corresponding to ZrO$_2$-65 mol% CeO$_2$ powder synthesized by CC method.

In Figure 1 can be observed that Fourier Transforms of the EXAFS signal corresponding to ZrO$_2$-65 mol% CeO$_2$ powder synthesized by GC method change qualitatively with temperature: while the peak close to R=4Å decrease with temperature, the peak close to R=3Å remains essentially without modifications. Between 600 and 800°C it is observed an inversion in amplitudes. This fact is related to changes in the second coordination shell of central Zr atom. Qualitative changes were also seen in the $\chi * k^3$ pattern. From XRD analysis, we found a t"→c transition close to 750°C for this powder.

CONCLUSIONS

It was observed that, for the same composition, the critic temperature (T_c) of the t'→t" or t"→c transition depends on the crystallite size. It was determined that the ZrO_2-65 mol% CeO_2 (GC) powder undergoes a t'→t" transition, and then a t"→c transition. From a qualitative analysis of the EXAFS signal, we observed a correlation between rearrangements in the local order of the second coordination shell of central zirconium atom and transitions observed by means of XRD analysis.

ACKNOWLEDGMENTS

The present work was supported by LNLS (Brazilian Synchrotron Light Laboratory, Brazil, proposals D04B-XAFS1-7225 and D10B-XPD7083). Fundación YPF (Beca Estenssoro 2005).

REFERENCES

1. D.G. Lamas et al., *J. Appl. Cryst.* **38**, 867-873 (2005).
2. I.O. Fabregas et al., *J. Phys.: Condens. Matter*, **18**, 7863-7881 (2006).
3. J. Kaspar et al., *Inorg. Chim. Acta.*, **349**, 217-226 (2003).

GISAXS Size Distribution Characterization of Cu Nanoparticles Embedded in silica

Ovidio Peña-Rodríguez[a], Luis Rodríguez-Fernández[b*], Vladimir Rodríguez-Iglesias[b], Guinther Kellermann[c], Alejandro Crespo-Sosa[b], Juan Carlos Cheang-Wong[b], Jesús Arenas-Alatorre[b], Alicia Oliver[b]

[a]Instituto de Investigaciones en Materiales, Universidad Nacional Autónoma de México, Apartado Postal 70-360, MéxicoD.F., 04510, Mexico.
[b]Instituto de Física, Universidad Nacional Autónoma de México, Apartado Postal 20-364, México, D.F., 01000, Mexico.
[c]Laboratório Nacional de Luz Síncrotron CP 6192, 13084-971 Campinas, SP, Brazil.
* Corresponding Author: Instituto de Física, UNAM, A.P. 20-364, México, D.F. 01000, Mexico. luisrf@fisica.unam.mx, Fax +52 55 56225009.

Abstract. Cu nanoparticles embedded in high purity silica produced by deep ion implantation at 2 MeV and located around 0.8 μm underneath the surface were analyzed by GISAXS and TEM. Same results were obtained by both techniques, indicating that GISAXS is a reliable method for shape and size characterization of metallic nanoclusters underneath the surface of a silica matrix. The Cu nanoparticles presented a nearly-spherical shape with a mean radius around 3 ± 1.2 nm.

Keywords: GISAXS, nanoparticles, implantation, TEM.
PACS: 07.85.Qe; 68.37.Lp; 78.67.Bf

INTRODUCTION

Metallic nanoparticles embedded in silica matrixes present linear and non-linear optical properties which are very promising for technological applications in optoelectronics devices [1,2]. From all the techniques used to obtain nanoparticles embedded in glasses, ion implantation stands for its several advantages, such as controllability of depth profile and concentration, high purity and the possibility to overcome low solubility restrictions. Particularly, deep ion implantation using energies in the order of MeV produces an ion depth distribution located some micrometers underneath the surface and wide enough which can be convenient for built optical waveguides.

The size and shape of nanoparticles can be characterized by transmission electron microscopy (TEM). However, TEM is a destructive method and sample preparation is difficult due to the mechanical properties of the silica matrix. In some cases the method used for sample preparation can induce changes in the characteristics of the nanoparticles. Also TEM is limited to the analysis of tiny spots and it does not give statistical information of the whole sample. On the other hand, Grazing Incidence

CP1092, Synchrotron Radiation in Materials Science: 6th International Conference, edited by R. Magalhaes-Paniago
© 2009 American Institute of Physics 978-0-7354-0625-4/09/$25.00

Small Angle X-ray Scattering is a versatile characterization technique for average size and shape, which enhance the signal scattered by the near surface region. This technique has been ideal for the analysis of implanted samples at typical keV energies where the ion distributions are in a region smaller than 0.5 μm beneath the surface. For MeV energies the implanted atoms are buried in the samples at the order of μm and covered by a layer with the same composition than the matrix. However this layer can carry defects created due to the ion irradiation [3]. Under this situation, GISAXS technique has to deal with scattering effects originated in this layer which can disturb the signal from the nanoparticles created by the implanted atoms.

In this work, Cu size nanoclusters synthesized by deep ion implantation and embedded in high purity silica were characterized by GISAXS and TEM in order to compare the results obtained by both techniques.

EXPERIMENTAL

The matrix of the samples consisted in polished flat squares plates of high purity synthetic silica ED-C grade made by Nippon Silica Glass, with OH content < 1 ppm and total impurity content < 20 ppm. The sizes of the square plates were 16x16 mm^2 and 1 mm thick. These silica squares were implanted by 2 MeV Cu ions tilting the normal of the samples 60° with respect to the incident beam at fluences of $0.6x10^{17}$ and $1.0x10^{17}$ ions/cm^2. These irradiations were carried out employing the Pelletron tandem accelerator at the Instituto de Física, UNAM. After implantation samples were cut in smaller pieces and annealed at 900°C in air during one hour in order to improve the Cu nanocluster formation.

Rutherford backscattering spectrometry (RBS) using 3 MeV $^4He^{+2}$ beam was performed using the same accelerator to determine the distributions of the Cu atoms inside the samples before and after the thermal annealing. The GISAXS technique was carried out at the XRD2 beam line of the National Synchrotron Light Laboratory (LNLS), Campinas, Brazil. A monochromatic 8 keV X-ray beam was used to analyze the size of the Cu nanoclusters. The X-ray dispersion patterns obtained were analyzed using the IsGISAXS v2.6 software [4]. The TEM analysis was performed at normal incidence with a point resolution of 1.9 Å using the JEOL2010 FEG instrument at the Instituto de Física, UNAM. Mechanical polished and ion milling with Ar$^+$ ion beam were used for the TEM samples preparation.

RESULTS

The RBS analysis indicates that the Cu implanted distribution in the silica is close to a Gaussian function with the maximum located at 0.7 μm underneath the surface and a FWHM of 0.58 μm. In this case the Cu nanoclusters region is buried by a silica layer of around 0.4 μm. After the thermal annealing the samples maintains the same Cu distribution.

Figure 1 shows the nanoparticles size distribution obtained by GISAXS for the two fluences. The experimental GISAXS dispersion patterns were compared to calculated fittings considering different shapes for the nanoparticles. The best adjustments were obtained considering spherical nanoparticles with a normal distribution of radii. For the samples of $0.6x10^{17}$ ions/cm2 the mean nanoclusters radius was 3.0 ± 1.2 nm, while for the $1.0x10^{17}$ ions/cm2 this radius was 3.3 ± 1.9 nm.

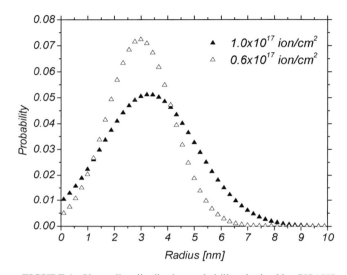

FIGURE 1. Size radius distribution probability obtained by GISAXS.

Figure 2 shows a low magnification TEM micrograph indicating the presence of Cu nanoclusters synthesized in the silica matrix. All the analyzed samples present a dominant formation of nanoparticles with nearly-spherical symmetric shapes. Figure 3 shows the histogram for the nanocluster radius obtained by TEM micrographs, (a) for the samples with $0.6x10^{17}$ ions/cm^2 and (b) for $1.0x10^{17}$ ions/cm^2. For both set of samples the radius distribution were around an average value of 3.2 nm but the size values are more spread for the samples with less fluence. The standard deviations were $\sigma = 1.8$ nm and $\sigma = 1.1$ nm for low and high fluence respectively.

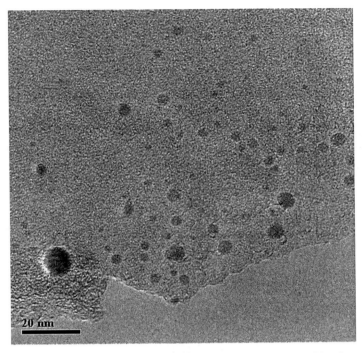

FIGURE 2. Low magnification TEM micrograph for a sample implanted with a fluence of $0.6x10^{17}$ ions/cm^2 [3].

CONCLUSIONS

The spherical shape and size values obtained by GISAXS are in good agreement with the ones obtained by TEM. This is an indication that there are not significant disturbing scattering effects originated in the layer over the Cu distribution and thermal annealing in air recovers the SiO$_2$ from de damage caused during implantation. In conclusion GISAXS is a reliable non-destructive characterization technique for metallic nanoparticles embedded in silica matrices produced by deep ion implantation.

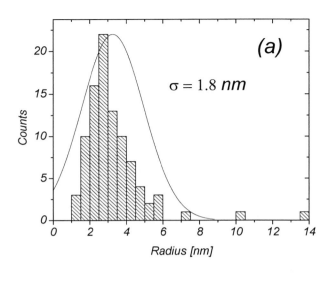

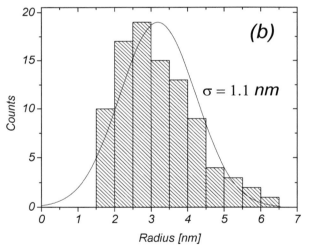

FIGURE 3. Histograms for the nanoclusters radius obtained by TEM micrographs: (a) for the samples with 0.6×10^{17} ions/cm^2 and (b) for 1.0×10^{17} ions/cm^2.

ACKNOWLEDGMENTS

We would like to thank K. López and F. J. Jaimes for the accelerator operation, J.G. Morales for the sample preparation and L. Rendón-Vázquez for TEM assistance. To the LNLS-Brazil for its assistance and support to this work, and to PAPIIT-UNAM under contract IN119706.

REFERENCES

1. F. Gonella and P. Mazzoldi, in: *Handbook of Nanostructured Materials and Nanotechnology*, H.S. Nalwa, Ed.; Academic Press, San Diego, 2000; Vol. 4, chap. 2.
2. E. Cattaruzza and F. Gonella, in: *Encyclopedia of Nanoscience and Nanotechnology*, H.S. Nalwa, Ed.; American Scientific Publishers, 2004; Vol. 5, pp. 369.
3. O. Peña; L. Rodríguez-Fernández; J.C. Cheang-Wong; P. Santiago; A. Crespo-Sosa; E. Muñoz; A. Oliver, *J. Non-Crystalline Solids* **352**, 349-354 (2006).
4. Rémi Lazzari, IsGISAXS, in electronic web page http://www.insp.upmc.fr/axe2/Oxydes/IsGISAXS/isgisaxs.htm.

Self-Assembly in Systems Containing Silicone Compounds

Maira Silva Ferreira* and Watson Loh

Instituto de Química, Universidade Estadual de Campinas (UNICAMP), Campinas – SP, Brasil
Caixa Postal 6154, CEP 13083-970, FAX 055193521302
mairasf@iqm.unicamp.br, wloh@iqm.unicamp.br

Abstract. Chemical systems formed by silicone solvents and surfactants have potential applications in a variety of industrial products. In spite of their technological relevance, there are few reports on the scientific literature that focus on characterizing such ternary systems. In this work, we have aimed to develop a general, structural investigation on the phase diagram of one system that typically comprises silicone-based chemicals, by means of the SAXS (small-angle X-ray scattering) technique. Important features such as the presence of diverse aggregation states in the overall system, either on their own or in equilibrium with other structures, have been detected. As a result, optically isotropic chemical systems (direct and/or reversed microemulsions) and liquid crystals with lamellar or hexagonal packing have been identified and characterized.

Keywords: silicone surfactants, mesophase, SAXS

PACS: 05.65.+b Self-organized systems

INTRODUCTION

The distinct behavior of silicones, as compared to that presented by hydrocabon solvents, is attributed to their low cohesive energy. As a result, water uptake in such solvents is impaired, but may be effected by employing silicone surfactants. In spite of their relevance, there have been very few reports on the characterization of these ternary systems[1]. In view of this, the present study aims to characterize a phase diagram of a system formed by a silicone oil (F244 Fluid, Dow Corning®), water and a commercial silicone surfactant (the superwetting agent Q2-5211, –OH end-capped and Additive 57, –OAc end-capped, both from Dow Corning®), focusing on the elucidation of self-assembled structures by small-angle X-ray scattering (SAXS).

RESULTS AND DISCUSSION

Figure 1 shows that some interesting results have been attained, as follows: the formation of microemulsion regions in opposite areas of the diagram, either water-rich (L₁) or oil-rich (L₂) environments, possessing low, although, variable viscosity; a broad liquid crystaline lamellar region; and a small region of hexagonal phase. With regards to the optically isotropic samples, the SAXS curves have confirmed the presence of aggregated structures showed a correlation distance between the drops in the range from 40 to 128Å.

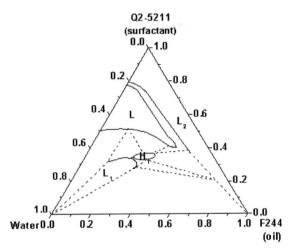

FIGURE 1 – Ternary phase diagram for the system formed with F244/water/Q2 at 25°C. L_1 (O/W microemulsion); L_2 (W/O microemulsion); L, (lamellar phase) and H_1 (normal hexagonal phase).

Figure 2 shows the formation of large microemulsion water-in-oil region (L_2) and mesophases such as lamellar (L) and reverse hexagonal (H_1). The isotropic samples showed a correlation distance between the drops in the range from 90 to 160Å.

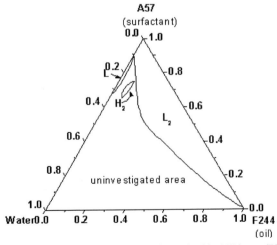

FIGURE 2 – Ternary phase diagram for the system formed with A57/water/F244 at 25°C. L_2 (W/O microemulsion); L (lamellar phase) and H_2 (reverse hexagonal phase).

CONCLUSION

End-capping groups have a significantly greater impact on the phase behavior than does the structure of the siloxane hydrophobe; changing the end group of the poly(oxyethylene) chain from –OH (Fig.1) to –OAc (Fig.2) changes the behavior of the phases. Both systems incorporate a high amount of water, 20 and 15% for Q2 and A57, respectively. Another aspect observed was the great diminution in the lamellar phase, for the end-capped surfactant.

ACKNOWLEDGMENTS

The authors are indebted to the following Brazilian institutions: CNPq (National Council of Scientific and Technological Development), for financial support, and LNLS (Brazilian Synchrotron Light Laboratory), for allocation of beam time during SAXS analyses.

REFERENCES

1. Hill; R.M.; He, M.; Davis, H.T., Screven, L.E.; *Langmuir*, 1994, *10*, 1725.

Structural characterization of La^{3+} modified Bi$_4$Ti$_3$O$_{12}$ ferroelectric ceramics by XRD and XAS techniques

V.B. Santos[1], M. Mir[2], V.R. Mastelaro[1], J.C. M'Peko[1], Y.P. Mascarenhas[1], A.C. Hernandes[1], P. P. Neves[2]

[1] Instituto de Física de São Carlos, Universidade de São Paulo, São Carlos-SP, Brazil,
[2] Departamento de Ciências Exatas - Efoa/Ceufe, Alfenas, MG, Brazil
vbsantos@ifsc.usp.br

Abstract. Bi$_{4x}$La$_x$Ti$_3$O$_{12}$ (BLT) ceramics were prepared and studied in this work in terms of La^{3+} modified the long and short range order structure. According to the results obtained from X-ray diffraction (XRD), the solubility limit (x_L) of La^{3+} into the Bi$_4$Ti$_3$O$_{12}$ (BIT) matrix was here found to locate slightly above $x = 1.5$ and all samples bellow this limit presents reflection peaks characteristic of the orthorhombic Bi$_4$Ti$_3$O$_{12}$ sample. X-ray absorption near edge spectra (XANES) shows that the local order around Ti, Bi and La atoms is not significantly affected by the increase of La amount as well as by the fact that La atoms could be located on different Bi sites.

Keywords: Ferroelectric ceramics, Long and short-range structures, X-ray diffraction, XANES,
PACS: 77.80.-e, 61.05.C-, 61.05.cj,

Introduction

Bismuth titanate (Bi$_4$Ti$_3$O$_{12}$, BIT) is a ferroelectric material with wide potential application in the electronic industry as capacitors, memory devices and sensors [1-2]. In order to improve the electrical properties of BIT, solid solutions with other cations have been considered and explored. This is the case of the La^{3+}–doped BIT (Bi$_{4-x}$La$_x$Ti$_3$O$_{12}$, BLT) system which has shown to improve, for $x = 0.75$ for instance, the fatigue endurance of the resulting material upon repeated cyclic electric fields. Nevertheless, in spite of the various studies that can be found so far in the literature, there appears to be no comprehensive work concerning the effect of the substitution of Ba by La atoms on the long and short-range order structure.

In the present work, we present results concerning the long and short-range order structure of Bi$_{4-x}$La$_x$Ti$_3$O$_{12}$ (BLT) ferroelectric ceramics which were respectively characterized by using X-ray diffraction and X-ray absorption spectroscopy techniques. These results are interpreted in terms of the physical properties of these samples.

EXPERIMENTAL

The studied materials were prepared through the conventional ceramic method starting from high-purity raw materials. Powders from these oxides were mixed according to the formula $[2-(x/2)]Bi_2O_3 + (x/2)La_2O_3 + 3TiO_2 \rightarrow Bi_{4-x}La_xTi_3O_{12}$, where x = 0, 0.5, 0.75, 1, 1.5 and 2, hereafter labeled as BLT100x, *i.e.*, BLT000 ≡ BIT, BLT050, BLT075, BLT100, BLT150 and BLT200, respectively.

The XRD measurements were done at the Brazilian Synchrotron Light Laboratory (LNLS) (D10B-XPD beam line). The XRD patterns were collected on a Huber diffractometer with geometry theta-2theta, λ =1.37787. Each pattern was measured from 8.5 to 110 in 2theta with step size of 0.005°. For this specific measurement, a Ge(111) analyzer was employed. X-ray absorption spectra at the Ti K-edge and La and Bi L$_{III}$-edges were measured at the D04B-XAFS1 beam line at the LNLS storage ring. The spectra were collected at room temperature using the transmission mode.

RESULTS AND DISCUSSION

XRD patterns of studied samples are characterized by reflection peaks isostructural with $Bi_4Ti_3O_{12}$ (BIT). Moreover, some low-intensity, additional peaks associated to impurity phases were detected in the XRD pattern of some samples.

The analysis of the XANES spectra at Ti K-edge (Figure 1), shows that the transitions associated with the symmetry of TiO6 octahedra (A and B peaks) are not significantly affected by the increasing of La amount as well as by the fact that La atoms are located at different Bi sites. However, some significative differences are observed at the XANES spectra region corresponding to atoms located at further shells.

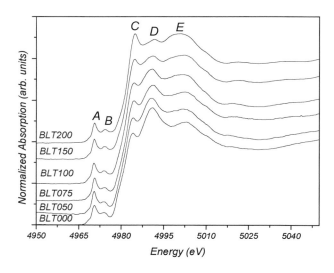

Figure 1 – Ti K-edge XANES spectra of BLT samples.

166

ACKNOWLEDGMENTS

The authors gratefully acknowledge the financial support from FAPESP, CNPQ and LNLS (Projects XPD#6517/07 and XAFS1#5937/06).

REFERENCES

1. J.M. Herbert, *Ferroelectric Transducers and Sensors*, Gordon and Breach Science Publishers, New York, 1982.
2. B.H. Park, B.S. Kang, S.D. Bu, T.W. Noh, J. Lee, and W. Jo, *Nature*, 1999, 401, 682-684.

Preparation and Characterization of Ti-Zr-V Non-Evaporable Getter Films to Be Used in Ultra-High Vacuum

Marcelo J. Ferreira[a], Denise A. Tallarico[b], Pedro A. P. Nascente[c]

[a]*Laboratório Nacional de Luz Sìncrotron, Rua Giuseppe Máximo Scolfaro, 10000
Pólo II de Alta Tecnologia de Campinas, Caixa Postal 6192 - CEP 13083-970, Campinas, SP,
Brazil, juni@lnls.br*
[b]*Universidade Federal de São Carlos, Programa de Pós-Graduação em Ciência e Engenharia
de Materiais, Via Washington Luis, km 235, CEP 13565-905, São Carlos, SP, Brazil,
deniseboni@yahoo.com.br*
[b]*Universidade Federal de São Carlos, Departamento de Engenharia de Materiais, Via
Washington Luis, km 235, CEP 13565-905, São Carlos, SP, Brazil, nascente@ufscar.br*

An appealing procedure to obtain operating pressures in the 10^{-8} Pa range, which is necessary for the insertion devices elements of synchrotron sources, is to coat the inner ultra-high vacuum chamber walls with a thin film of non-evaporable getter (NEG) metals. Titanium, zirconium, vanadium, and their alloys are used as NEG materials due to their low activation temperature, high chemical activity, large solubility, and high diffusivity for gases. In this work, magnetron sputtering was employed to deposit thin films of Ti-Zr-V on a Si(111) substrate. The morphological, structural, and chemical analyses were carried out by atomic force microscopy (AFM), scanning electron microscopy (SEM) with energy-dispersive spectroscopy (EDS), and X-ray photoelectron spectroscopy (XPS).

Keywords: Non-evaporable getter, NEG, coatings, thin films, ultra-high vacuum, synchrotron.

PACS: 68.55.-a; 81.15.Cd; 81.05.Bx; 07.30.Kf.

INTRODUCTION

The construction of ultra-high vacuum (UHV) chambers for particle accelerators requires the use of operating pressures in the 10^{-8} Pa range. In particular, it is difficult to obtain this vacuum level for chambers with a length to transverse section rate of 150:1, as can be found in insertion devices elements of synchrotron sources. An appealing procedure to obtain this condition is to coat the inner chamber walls with a thin film of NEG metals [1-10]. Usually the NEG coatings are constituted by elements of great reactivity and solubility (such as Ti, Zr, and V) at room temperature [3]. Hydrogen, carbon monoxide, carbon dioxide, and other molecules encountered in UVH diffuse readily into the NEG coatings. Heating the NEG in UHV will cause desorption of molecules from the surface or diffusion of them into the bulk, in the so-called activation process [5]. In this work, magnetron sputtering was employed to deposit thin films of Ti-Zr-V on a Si(111) substrate. The morphological, structural, and chemical analyses were carried out by AFM, SEM/EDS, and XPS, respectively.

CP1092, *Synchrotron Radiation in Materials Science: 6th International Conference*, edited by R. Magalhaes-Paniago
© 2009 American Institute of Physics 978-0-7354-0625-4/09/$25.00

The samples were heat treated at 100, 200, 300, 400, and 500 °C in UHV in order to evaluate the absorption process. The produced materials (TiZrV/LNLS) were compared to a commercial TiZrV sample (TiZrV/SAES), and this comparison made clear that the desired characteristics are related to the nanometric structure of the films, and that he structure is sensitive to the heat treatments.

RESULTS

Figure 1 displays AFM micrographs of the two thin films, TiZrV/LNLS (a) and TiZrV/SAES (b). It can be observed rough films with peaks of 80 nm. The TiZrV/LNLS film presented less uniform, higher and thinner grains compared to the TiZrV/SAES sample, indicating larger roughness, smaller grain size, and larger surface area. These characteristics are very interesting for NEG applications.

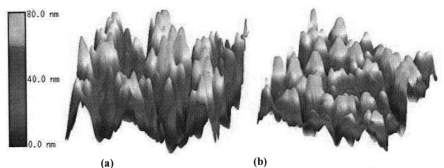

(a)   **(b)**
FIGURE 1. 3D AFM images of (a) TiZrV/LNLS and (b) TiZrV/SAES films

To verify the behavior of absorption of the thin film, XPS analyses were carried out for the TiZrV/LNLS film as-deposited and after heating. The sample was heated in UHV at 200, 300, 400, and 500 °C for 24 hours. Figures 2, 3, and 4 present the XPS Ti 2p, Zr 3d, and V 2p spectra, respectively. In Figures 2 and 3, it can be observed that either Ti or Zr did not change chemically, remaining as TiO_2 and ZrO_2 for all temperatures employed in the heat treatment. Slight differences in the XPS V 2p spectra obtained for the TiZrV/LNLS film before and after heat treatment can be observed in Fig. 4, indicating changes in the chemical state of vanadium.

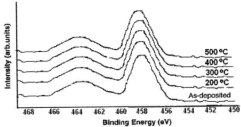

FIGURE 2. XPS Ti 2p spectra obtained for the as-deposited film and after heating at 200, 300, 400, and 500°C for 24 hours.

169

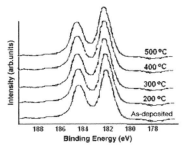

FIGURE 3. XPS Zr 3d spectra obtained for the as-deposited film and after heating at 200, 300, 400, and 500°C for 24 hours.

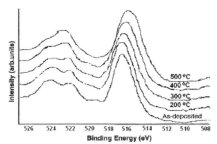

FIGURE 4. XPS V 2p spectra obtained for the as-deposited film and after heating at 200, 300, 400, and 500°C for 24 hours.

The compositions (atomic %) were measured by XPS to be 20Ti-30Zr-50V, for the NEG film produced at LNLS, and 26Ti-29Zr-45V, for the commercial film.

EDS analyses were performed on the TiZrV/LNLS film before and after heating in order to measure the amount of oxygen present in the bulk of the film (in cross-section). The results are presented in Table 1 and indicate that oxygen was absorbed into the bulk of the film.

TABLE 1. Oxygen percentages measured by EDS in cross-section for the TiZrV/LNLS films.

TiZrV/LNLS film	Oxygen (atomic %)
As-deposited	8
After heat treatment	68

Figure 5 shows SEM micrographs of the TiZrV/LNLS film (a) before and (b) after heat treatment; the inserts display the respective cross section views. For the as-deposited film (Fig. 5(a)), the micrograph presents small grains and considerable porosity; the cross section view (insert of Fig. 5(a)) indicates a columnar growth of spaced grains having small diameters. The heat treatment caused densification of the film by the growth of the grains, as shown if Fig. 5(b) and its insert.

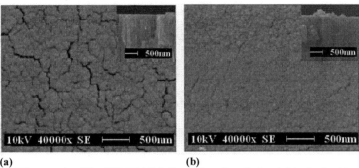

(a)   (b)

FIGURE 5. Micrographs of the TiZrV/LNLS film: (a) as-deposited and (b) after heat treatment.

DISCUSSION

AFM images revealed that the films produced at LNLS presented roughness and grain size values comparable to those of the commercial NEG sample. SEM micrographs showed that the heat treatment caused an increase in the grain size and a decrease in the porosity of the NEG/LNLS films. EDS results indicated the absorption of oxygen into the NEG bulk. XPS results showed that the film surface was oxidized, and that the heat treatment at 200, 300, 400, and 500 °C for 24 hours did not change the oxidation states for both Ti and Zr, and caused only a slight change for V. The characteristics of the NEG films produced at LNLS were similar to those of the commercial sample.

CONCLUSIONS

The film of TiZrV produced in the LNLS presented compatible properties with the film produced by the largest worldwide producer of NEGs, the SAES Getters. The results indicate that the TiZrV/LNLS film presents the necessary requirements for application as NEG. The significant changes in the amount of oxygen present in the bulk indicate that the film absorbed oxygen during the heat treatment. This heat treatment aged the film due to the diminution of porosity and, consequently, the reduction in storage capacity of the pores.

ACKNOWLEDGMENTS

This work was supported by the Laboratório Nacional de Luz Síncrotron, FAPESP, CAPES, and CNPq of Brazil. The authors would like to thank SAES Getter Spa. for a NEG sample.

REFERENCES

1. C. Benvenuti, P. Chiggiato, F. Cicoira, Y. L'Aminot, J. Vac. Sci. Technol. A 16, 148 (1998).
2. A. E. Prodromides, C. Scheuerlein, M. Taborelli, Vacuum 60, 35-41 (2001).
3. C. Benvenuti *et alli*, Vacuum 60, 57-65 (2001).
4. V. Matolin, V. Johanek, Vacuum 67, 177 (2003).
5. C. Benvenuti *et alli*, Vacuum 71, 307 (2003).
6. J. Zemeck, P. Jiricek, Vacuum 71, 329 (2003).
7. K. M. Welch, J. Vac. Sci. Technol. A 21, S19 (2003).
8. C.-C. Li *et alli*, Surf. Coat. Technol. 200, 1351 (2005).
9. C.-C. Li *et alli*, Surf. Coat. Technol. 201, 3977 (2006).
10. P. Chiggiato, P. Costa Pinto, Thin Solid Films 515, 382 (2006).

Complex salts formed by anionic copolymers with hexadecyltrimethylammonium: Phase equilibrium and structural characterization using SAXS.

Ana Maria Percebom, Juliana S. Bernardes and Watson Loh*.

Institute of Chemistry – Universidade Estadual de Campinas (UNICAMP), P.O.Box 6154, Zip Code 13083-970, Campinas, Brazil, FAX 055193521-3023
quimica_ana@yahoo.com.br, julianab@iqm.unicamp.br, wloh@iqm.unicamp.br

Abstract. Extending earlier studies conducted by this research group about the hexadecyltrimethylammonium (CTA^+) and other poly-anions in water, this study aims at analyzing the phase equilibrium and characterizing structures of mesophases formed by mixtures of oppositely charged surfactants and polymers. Its specific objective is to verify the effect of the charge density along the poly-electrolyte. Poly(4-styrenesulfonic acid-co-maleic acid), P(SS-AM), was used because this copolymer has three acid groups with different pKa values, enabling to obtain negative charges in all groups or only in a few. The self-assembly of the complex salt (anionic copolymer + cationic surfactant) was investigated in binary (+ water) and ternary systems (+ water + 1-decanol), determining their phase diagrams and analyzing the structures of mesophases formed by SAXS.

Keywords: Surfactant mesophases, Surfactant-Polymers mixtures, SAXS
PACS: 05.65.+b Self-organized systems

INTRODUCTION

The addition of poly-electrolytes to systems containig oppositely charged surfactants changes their self-assembly properties and may precipitate a complex-salt (poly-electrolyte + surfactant). In solution, the complex molecules are capable of forming micelles with several geometrical forms. These micelles can be periodically organized, leading to the development of liquid crystalline mesophases. Small Angle X-Ray Scattering (SAXS) measurements give structural information about the several systems formed. This project seeks to investigate how anionic copolymers with different charge densities can affect the self-assembly properties of CTA^+. The copolymer poly(4-styrenesulfonic acid-co-maleic acid), P(SS-AM), was used to prepare the complex-salt CTAP(SS-AM) in water and in the presence of a co-surfactant (1-decanol).

CP1092, *Synchrotron Radiation in Materials Science: 6th International Conference*, edited by R. Magalhaes-Paniago

RESULTS AND DISCUSSION

In this work, the method developed by Piculell[1] is used to produce the pure complex-salt to reduce the number of the system components. CTAP(SS-AM) has been synthesized at pH = 3. Titration curves indicate that only one of the maleic acid groups is not bound to CTA^+. CTAP(SS-AM) has been used to prepare samples with different amounts of water to study the binary system. In concentrations higher than 61% (wt.%) of complex-salt, there is a birefringent phase, and in concentrations between 30% e 61% (wt.%) a very viscous isotropic phase is formed. SAXS measurements indicate that the birefringent phase presents hexagonal structure, but the isotropic phase diffractogram shows only an intense correlation peak (Figure 1). It means that the system contains non-structured cylindrical micelles. In concentrations below 30% (wt.%), the system displays a liquid isotropic (micellar) phase in equilibrium with the viscous one.

Samples of the ternary system have been prepared with the co-surfactant 1-decanol. With the alcohol addition, a predominant lamellar phase is observed. It was not possible to observe the formation of a system with aggregates totally soluble in 1-decanol (L_2).

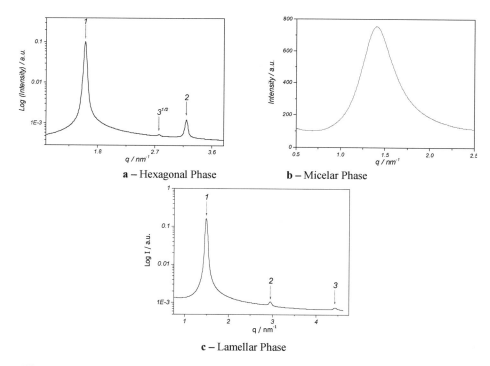

a – Hexagonal Phase   **b** – Micelar Phase

c – Lamellar Phase

Figure 1 – SAXS diffractograms of: **a** – Hexagonal Phase; **b** – Micelar Phase; **c** – Lamellar Phase.

CONCLUSION

The electrical charges present in the complex-salt favor the aggregates soluble in water and do not display the formation of aL_2 phase. Addition of 1-decanol leads to formation of a lamellar phase formation because of the co-surfactant effect.

ACKNOWLEDGMENTS

The authors gratefully acknowledge FAPESP and CNPq for financial support and the LNLS for the use of the SAXS beamline and the support of the line staff.

REFERENCES

1. L. Picullel; A. Svensson; J. Norman; J.S. Bernardes; L. Karlsson; W. Loh *Pure Appl. Chem.* 2002, *79*, 1419

An EXAFS Study Of The Binding Of Chromium, Mercury And Copper On Natural, Crosslinked And Multilayer Chitosan Films

Rafael Gonçalves de Paiva[a], Rodrigo Silveira Vieira[a], Cassiano Gomes Aimoli[a] and Marisa Masumi Beppu[a]

[a] *School of Chemical Engineering, State University of Campinas, P.O. Box 6066, Zip code 13081-970, Campinas, SP, Brazil. E-mail: beppu@feq.unicamp.br*

Abstract. The coordination environment of metal atoms involved in their adsorption on chitosan was studied by using EXAFS technique. Chromium, mercury and copper complexes were gotten on natural, crosslinked and multilayer chitosan films and the spectra of the distribution of neighbor atoms around the adsorbed central atom were obtained. All spectra were obtained in transmission mode and were collected around Hg (12284eV) L edge, Cr (5989eV) and Cu (8987eV) K edges. For chromium ions, it was possible to observe that metal interaction is mainly performed on amino groups, on the other hand, it was not possible to distinguish if the metal interaction takes place preferentially on amino or hydroxyl group, for mercury and copper.

Keywords: Copper, Chitosan, Alginate, Films

PACS: 80.82.35.Pq

INTRODUCTION

Chitosan and alginate have been described as suitable biopolymers for removal of heavy metal ions from wastewater [1-3], since its chemical groups can act as chelating sites. Most of the studies on heavy metal adsorption have been dedicated to the determination of the overall uptake performance; however, there is limited information available on identifying the adsorption mechanism.

Extended X-Ray absorption fine structure (EXAFS) spectroscopy was used to provide information about the coordination environment and the nearest neighboring atoms involved in the heavy metal ion adsorption on biopolymer films [4].

Four different chitosan films were produced:

- Natural chitosan;
- Gluataraldehyde-crosslinked chitosan;
- Epichlorohydrin-crosslinked chitosan;
- Multilayer chitosan/alginate film;

All types of films were soaked in 1000ppm of Hg(II), Cr(VI) or Cu(II) solution, in order to promote the adsorption of ions onto each polymeric matrix.

CP1092, *Synchrotron Radiation in Materials Science: 6th International Conference*, edited by R. Magalhaes-Paniago
© 2009 American Institute of Physics 978-0-7354-0625-4/09/$25.00

EXAFS experiments were carried out at Brazilian National Synchrotron Light Laboratory (LNLS), using a channel-cut Si (111) monochromator. Standard compounds were used in order to distinguish the heavy metal and coordination spheres. To treat the EXAFS data, the standard compounds were initially analyzed. The data were analyzed using ATHENA® and ARTEMIS® software (IFEFFIT package).

RESULTS

The results obtained from the EXAFS analysis (related to copper interactions with chitosan and multilayer chitosan/alginate films) are shown below.

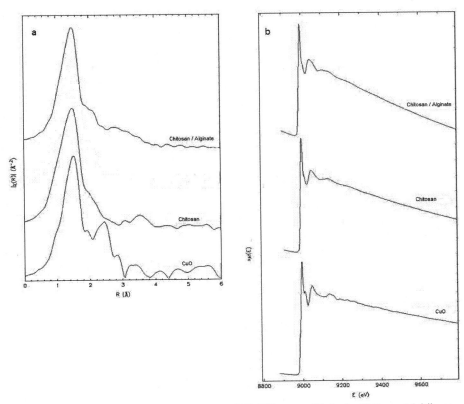

FIGURE 1. Radial distribution function (a) and EXAFS spectra (b) for the Chitosan, Multilayer Chitosan Alginate and Standard Copper Oxide samples.

For films with chromium, EXAFS analysis showed similar results for natural and crosslinked films, if compared to standard compounds (Cr_2O_3), with a strong peak at about 1.3 Å and a weak peak at about 1.7 Å. The opposite was observed for glutaraldehyde-crosslinked chitosan. There is the first metal coordination sphere at a distance of about 1.3 Å and a second metal coordination sphere (in small proportion) at a distance of about 1.7 Å.

After crosslinking with epichlorohydrin, the hydroxyl groups of chitosan structure are unavailable and amino groups are free. Comparing the absorption spectra for natural and epichlorohydrin-crosslinked chitosan, a similar profile con be observed [5].

For films with mercury, by analyzing the structure of natural chitosan, it is possible to observe that amino and hydroxyl groups are available and they are the main adsorption sites. In the Fourier-transformed graph for natural chitosan three peaks at R < 2.0 Å were observed and a lower peak at about 2.1 Å was also observed. For epichlorohydrin and glutaraldehyde-crosslinked chitosan only two peaks at R < 2.0 Å and a decrease of intensity in the peak at about 2.1 Å were observed [5].

Finally, for films with copper, a strong peak was observed, in all chitosan films, at approximately 1.5 Å (first metal coordinate sphere) indicating that the copper on the adsorbent may be bound to either an oxygen or nitrogen. In the present study, for each metal, the same signal was observed practically in all samples, either natural, crosslinked chitosan and chitosan/alginate multilayer films, indicating that adsorption takes place either on amino or hydroxyl groups in all samples, since is observed the same peak at about 1.9-2.1 Å [5].

DISCUSSION

It was expected that the adsorption mechanism for chromium, mercury and copper ions is different in each type of chitosan membrane, since the chemical modification on chitosan can take place in amino or hydroxyl groups. However, the chemical modification presented a greater effect for chromium ions. The qualitative comparison of spectra could indicate that chromium ions produce, probably, the same structure after metal and chitosan interaction, for natural chitosan and epichlorohydrin-crosslinked chitosan, indicating that amino groups may play a significant role in this process. For copper and mercury ions, it was not possible to distinguish if the adsorption occurs mainly on amino or hydroxyl groups, although it indicated that the interaction between chitosan and alginate chains can act like a crosslinking effect.

CONCLUSIONS

EXAFS con be a powerful technique to qualitatively analyze the mechanism of metal ion adsorption onto chitosan films. The structure of heavy metal ions on chitosan adsorbents depends on chemical modification of polymeric matrix, or primarily on the chemical groups available in the polymeric matrices. For chromium, amino groups seems to be the most important adsorption site. For mercury and copper ions it was not possible to distinguish if the metal interaction takes place preferentially on amino or hydroxyl groups, being necessary to use this technique along with others like FTIR and XPS.

ACKNOWLEDGMENTS

The authors thank LNLS – Brazilian National Synchrotron Light Laboratory, for the EXAFS analysis, FAPESP, CAPES and CNPq for financial support.

REFERENCES

1. E. Guibal, Sep. Purif. Technol, 38, 43-74 (2004).
2. R.S. Vieira, M.M. Beppu, Water Res., 40(8), 1726-1734 (2006).
3. R.S. Vieira, M.M. Beppu, Colloids and Surfaces A: Physichochem. Eng. Aspects, 279, 196-207 (2006).
4. N.V. Kramareva, A. Y.. Stakheev, O. P. Tkachenko, K.V. Klementiev, W. Grünert, E. D. Finashina and L. M. Kustov, Journal of Molecular Catalysis A: Chemical 209, 97–106 (2004).
5. R.S. Vieira, E. Meneghetti, C.G. Aimoli, G.A.S. Goulart and M.M. Beppu, An EXAFS Study of the Binding of Chromium, Mercury and Copper on Natural and Crosslinked Chitosan Films. In: 10th International Conference on Chitin and Chitosan / 7ht International Conference of the European Chitin Society, 2006, Montpellier/France. 10th I.C.C.C / EUCHIS 06, 2006. p. 765-771.

Smectic ordering in polymer liquid crystal-silica aerogel nanocomposites. Studies of DSC and SAXS.

Nádya Pesce da Silveira[£]*, Françoise Ehrburger-Dolle[#], Cyrille Rochas[#], Arnaud Rigacci[§], Fabiano Vargas Pereira[$], Aloir Antonio Merlo[£] and Harry Westfahl Jr.[&]

[£]*Universidade Federal do Rio Grande do Sul, Instituto de Química, Av. Bento Gonçalves 9500 Porto Alegre - Rio Grande do Sul, CEP 91501 970 Caixa Postal 15003, Brazil (nadya@iq.ufrgs.br)*
[#]*Laboratoire de Spectrométrie Physique, Université Joseph Fourier, France (francoise.ehrburger-dolle@ujf-grenoble.fr)*
[§]*CENERG, École des Mines de Paris,Sophia-Antipolis, France (arnaud.rigacci@cenerg.cma.fr)*
[$]*Universidade do Estado da Bahia, Salvador, Brasil (fvpereira@uneb.br)*
[&]*Laboratório Nacional de Luz Síncrotron, Campinas, Brazil (westfahl@lnls.br)*

Abstract. Two series of side chain liquid crystal (SCLC) polyacrylate-silica aerogel nanocomposites have been investigated by small-angle x-ray scattering (SAXS) and differential scanning calorimetry (DSC). The first series (*ex-situ* nanocomposite) was obtained by infiltration of a smectic SCLC polyacrylate prepared by polymerisation in solution into monolithic aerogel slabs. The second one (*in-situ* nanocomposite) was prepared by photopolymerisation of the monomer infiltrated in the aerogel. The results are compared with those obtained for bulk polyacrylates. It is shown that the smectic ordering is not destroyed by confinement in the aerogel. Spacing of the smectic layers and smectic correlation lengths were deduced from the fit of the SAXS profiles to a Lorentzian function with a quadratic correction. The principal results suggest that *in-situ* polymerisation enhances the degree of order and the stability of the smectic phase in the nanocomposite.

Keywords: polymer liquid-crystal, nanocomposite, xerogel.
PACS: 33.20.Rm (X-ray spectra), 36.20.Kd (Electronic structure and spectra)

INTRODUCTION

Research on the confinement of thermotropic liquid crystalline (LC) systems is being largely developed as a consequence of possible applications. Confinement breaks the symmetry of the LC and allows a larger surface-to-volume ratio if compared to the bulk.[1] The ordering of the LC molecules as well as their susceptibility to external fields is affected, transforming the composite into a potential material for electro-optical applications.[1] The purpose of this paper is to sheed some light on the thermotropic behaviour of smectic polymers confined in a silica aerogel. The starting chiral acrylate monomer has a spacer containing eleven carbons.[2] Bulk side-chain liquid crystal (SCLC) polyacrylates were prepared by polymerisation in solution and

CP1092, *Synchrotron Radiation in Materials Science: 6th International Conference*, edited by R. Magalhaes-Paniago
© 2009 American Institute of Physics 978-0-7354-0625-4/09/$25.00

by UV photopolymerisation. Confinement was achieved either by infiltration of polymer (*ex-situ* nanocomposite) or by infiltration of monomer followed by photopolymerisation (*in-situ* nanocomposite). All samples were analysed by small angle x-ray scattering (SAXS) measurements. Thermotropic behaviour of the samples was probed by differential scanning calorimetry (DSC). As preliminary measurements[3,4] have shown, confined polyacrylates keep liquid crystalline behaviour, with crystalline state (K) → smectic (S) mesophase transition temperatures shifted to smaller values than in bulk.

EXPERIMENTAL

Samples were prepared either by confinement of previously synthesized SCLC or by photopolymerization of the mesogenic moieties derived from phenyl benzoate, inside 1.5 mm thick discs of porous silica aerogels. The aerogels have a mean pore size of 12 nm and mass density $\rho = 0.19$ g/cm^3. SAXS measurements were performed at the ESRF, Grenoble, on beamline BM2. The incident energy was 16.2 keV.

	M_n	M_w/M_n	K		Sm		I
POA	21200	1.60	•	310	•	337	•
PIA	21200	1.60	•	306	•	333	•
PPOA	*	*	•	310	•	*	•
PPIA	*	*	•	303	•	334	•

Table 1 –Molecular weight and transition temperatures (K) for the liquid crystal polymers (SCLC) and composites.

The scattering curve I(q) was determined over a domain of q values ranging between 0.03 and 1.10 Å^{-1}.

Differential Scanning Calorimetry (DSC) was used to determine the transition temperatures. Table 1 gives some polymers characteristics and Figure 1 gives some SAXS profiles from different samples.

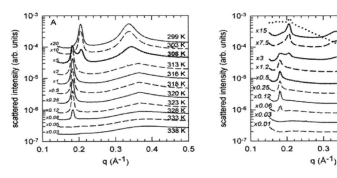

Figure 1 – SAXS profiles determined at different temperature: A) SCLC polyacrylate photopolymerised in bulk (PPOA); B) SCLC polyacrylate photopolymerised inside the aerogel (PPIA) after subtraction of the aerogel scattering background.

RESULTS AND CONCLUSIONS

To perform the analysis of the shape of the smectic peaks located around 0.18 $\mathring{A}^1$, the contribution of the polymer backbone must be subtracted from the measured intensity. Instead of using a model equation to fit the scattering due to the backbone conformation, a simple polynomial equation $a+bq^2+cq^4$ was used over a limited q-interval. The lower limit, q_{min}, is located above the smectic peak (around 0.24 $\mathring{A}^1$) and the upper limit, q_{max} (around 0.3 $\mathring{A}^1$), below the maximum of the diffuse peak. This equation was used for extrapolation down to low-q values and the corresponding intensities were subtracted from the experimental ones, yielding the peak plotted in Figure 5 (filled circles). The peaks were then fitted with an empirical function as follows

$$I = \frac{\sigma}{\left(q^2 - q_0^2\right)^2 + 4q_0^2\xi^{-2}} \tag{1}$$

σ corresponds to a smectic susceptibility at the ordering vector q_0 and ξ is the length of the smectic correlation. The choice of this function was made empirically, starting from a Lorentzian function, which fitted well the data around q_0.

The values of d extracted from the fits are plotted in Figure 2 as a function of the reduced temperature.

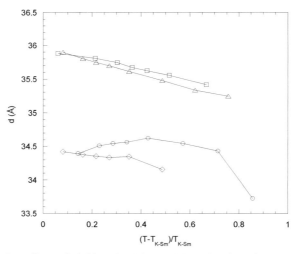

Figure 2 – Lamellae period d for POA ($\triangle$), PIA ($\square$), PPOA ($\lozenge$) and PPIA ($\circ$). $T_{K\text{-Sm}}$ is the K→Sm transition temperature corresponding to each sample.

Figure 3 shows the variation of the correlation length ξ obtained for the four samples as a function of the temperature. For sample POA, the value of ξ and its temperature behaviour is different from that of all other samples. As expected from the above comments, ξ remains almost constant (~ 360 $\mathring{A}$) and starts to decrease on approaching the melting temperature T_I. Confinement (sample PIA) of this polymer leads to a smaller value of ξ (~ 200 Å) that begins to decrease at a lower temperature than for POA. The small value of ξ (~ 250 Å) obtained for PPOA can be attributed to the high degree of chain entanglements already mentioned. The temperature behaviour of ξ for the *in-situ* nanocomposite PPIA is again different from that of the other samples since ξ increases from a small value (~160 Å) up to nearly that observed for POA. Thus, the degree of chain entanglement will not be increased by photopolymerisation in the aerogel over that photopolymerised in bulk (PPOA). Hence, photopolymerisation in an aerogel allows the establishment of a stable lamellae organisation in the polymer, similar to that observed for POA. The corresponding temperature domain, however is narrow.

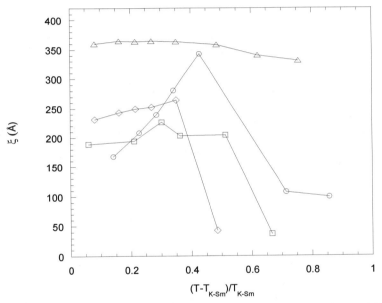

Figure 3 – Correlation lengths ξ measured for POA (Δ), PIA (□), PPOA (◊) and PPIA (○). $T_{K\text{-}Sm}$ is the K→Sm transition temperature.

CONCLUSIONS

Ex-situ and *in-situ* side chain liquid crystal (SCLC) polyacrylate-silica aerogel nanocomposites were successfully prepared by infiltration of a silica aerogel with polymer and by photopolymerisation of infiltrated monomer, respectively. The main characteristics of the SmA_1 mesophase of the bulk polyacrylates are maintained for the polymers in the nanocomposites. Confinement shifts the temperature domain of the smectic phase to lower temperatures. The smectic ordering of the polymer confined in the aerogel is short-ranged, with a correlation length that increases with increasing temperature, which is opposite to the behaviour observed for low molar mass nematogenics. For the *in-situ* nanocomposite, the temperature dependence of the smectic layer spacing d as well as that of the correlation length ξ are remarkably different from that of the other samples. This feature suggests that *in-situ* polymerisation enhances the degree of order and smectic phase stability in the system.

This research is a first step for the challenge of liquid crystal polymer-aerogels composites. Knowledge about the strengths and weaknesses of this kind of systems towards applications may be achieved through confinement of liquid crystal polymers having different chemical composition and thermotropic behaviour.

ACKNOWLEDGEMENTS

The authors are grateful to the ESRF, Grenoble, for access to the French CRG beamline. Prof. O. M. Ritter for synthesis and the CAPES/COFECUB program (411/03) for financial support.

REFERENCES

1. A. G. Rappaport, N. A. Clark, B. N. Thomas and T. Bellini, Liquid Crystals in Complex Geometries Formed by Polymer and Porous Networks, Taylor & Francis, London, 1996, Chapter 20, p. 411..
2. O. M. Ritter, A. A. Merlo, F. V. Pereira, N. P. da Silveira, E. Geissler and J. Zukerman-Schpector, *Liquid Crystals*, 2002, *61*, 1187.
3. N. P. Silveira, F. Ehrburger-Dölle, C. Rochas, A. Rigacci, F. V. Pereira, H. Westfahl Jr., *J. Therm. Anal. Cal.*, 2005, *79*, 579.
4. N. P. Silveira, F. V. Pereira, A. A. Merlo, F. Bley, I. Morfin, O. M. Ritter, F. Ehrburger-Dölle, *Liquid-Crystals*, 2008, *35*, 299.

X-ray Absorption Spectroscopic Studies of Tl-Based High Temperature Superconductors

Arvind Agarwal [a] and A.N.Vishnoi [b]

[a]Department of Physics, M.N. National Institute of Technology, Allahabad 211004, INDIA.
[b]Department of Physics, University of Allahabad, Allahabad 211002, INDIA

Abstract. The position, shape and EXAFS of X-ray absorption discontinuities have been used to deduce structural and chemical bonding information on thallium superconducting cuperates. The superconducting cuperates of composition $Tl_{1-x}V_xSr_2(Ca_{0.8}Y_{0.2})Cu_2O_7$ (x = 0.2, 0.3, 0.4, 0.5) have been examined to investigate the atomic environment around thallium ion on vanadium doping on its site. The data obtained were analyzed by Fourier transform. The coordination number (N), average radial distance (R) and the total phase shift (σ) experienced by photoelectron for thallium compounds have been reported. The results show that the substitution of vanadium at Tl site does not change the local environment around thallium ion.

Keywords: EXAFS, Thallium, Superconductors.
PACS: 61.05.cj, 78.70.Dm

INTRODUCTION

Since the discovery of superconductivity in the La-Ba-Cu-O and Y-Ba-Cu-O systems, there has been extensive research on the substitution of 3 d transition metals. A large number of 3 d transition metal cations have accessible valencies of four and above. This suggests that the high valent 3 d transition metals might play the same role as lead (4+) if they substitute for Tl(3+) sites in $TlSr_2CaCu_2O_7$ rather than substituting in the Cu-O framework. This substitution may reduce the over doping of $TlSr_2CaCu_2O_7$ and give rise to a superconductor.

We have studied four superconducting oxides of the composition $(Tl_{1-x}V_x)$ Sr_2 $(Ca_{0.8}Y_{0.2})$ Cu_2O_7 (x=0.2, 0.3, 0.4 and 0.5) in order to study atomic environment of vanadium ions. The single structure data are not available on these superconducting oxides. The structural information on these oxides have been obtained by recording EXAFS of thallium L_{III} edge and analyzing the data using Fourier transform and non-linear curve fitting techniques. The Tl_2O_3 was used as model compound containing Tl-O atom pair.

The data analyzed were collected in the in-house EXAFS laboratory. X-rays emitted from a conventional X-ray tube were monochromatised by a flat silicon (1,1,1) crystal and allowed to pass through the sample. The transmitted X-rays were then detected through a detector by moving the sample in and out of the X-ray beam. The voltage pulses produced were fed in to a digital scalar and counted for a certain time; the number of counts per unit time was directly proportional to the number of photons entering into the detector. The ratio of counts of detector reading without the sample and with the sample gave I_o/I. The logarithm of this value was proportional to

CP1092, *Synchrotron Radiation in Materials Science: 6th International Conference,* edited by R. Magalhaes-Paniago

the absorption coefficient μ. The (I_o/I) was then recorded as a function of the monochromator crystal position. The crystal was mounted on a goniometer driven by a stepping motor. The monochromator steps were proportional to the incident angle of the X-ray beam on the crystal face. The data analyzed was originally in the form of monochromator steps versus I_o/I.

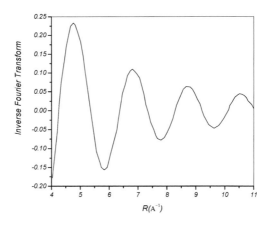

FIGURE 1. Inverse Fourier transform (***) and simulated EXAFS of the first FT peak (solid line) for $(Tl_{0.8}V_{0.2})$ Sr_2 $(Ca_{0.8}Y_{0.2})$ Cu_2O_7

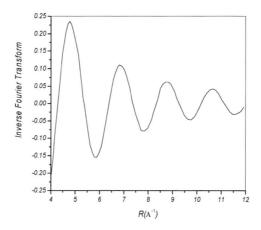

FIGURE 2. Inverse Fourier transform (***) and simulated EXAFS of the first FT peak (solid line) for $(Tl_{0.5}V_{0.5})$ Sr_2 $(Ca_{0.8}Y_{0.2})$ Cu_2O_7

186

RESULTS

In a model system Tl_2O_3 the crystallographic data coordination number N; bond distance R and Debye Waller type factor σ are known. Therefore Tl_2O_3 EXAFS spectrum was used to generate a set of self–consistent scattering parameters which were transformed to an unknown system of similar chemical nature. A least squares procedure was set up to minimize the variance. The Fourier transforms of the L_{III} edge EXAFS data in Tl_2O_3 show three distinct peaks. The first peak is the dominant one and corresponds to Tl-O distance. This peak was then inverse Fourier transformed to yield the contribution of backscatters about Tl^{+++} ions.

The structural parameters for Tl_2O_3 were used in the curve fitting analysis of Fourier filtered EXAFS. The first radial peak of the Fourier transform for Tl_2O_3 corresponds to the shell of six O atoms about the absorbing Tl atom. The self-consistent phase for the Tl-O pair was obtained using parameterized values of phase shift φ. The envelope function for oxygen was obtained empirically from the filtered EXAFS itself, and was fixed in the simulation, the inner potential or the threshold energy required to determine the value of photoelectron wave vector k, was found to be 12671 eV. It is obtained after matching the peaks in imaginary part [1] and the modulus of the Fourier transform (N=6 and R=2.25 Å) were used as fixed structural parameters. The thermal parameter σ was varied. The simulation was done in k space to emphasize the backscattering contribution of O at low k.

DISCUSSION

The plot of experimental phase shift versus wave vector k for Tl-O atom pair obtained in simulation was very close to that obtained from theoretical values given by Teo & Lee [2]. The data of Fourier transform for the vanadium doped superconducting oxides of thallium were interpreted using Fourier filtered data from Tl_2O_3. A non linear least squares fitting technique was then employed to match the calculated χ to the measured one obtained from inverse Fourier transform of the first peak (Figure 1, Figure 2).

The calculated oxygen members of 2.30 and 2.10 in the first coordination shell for superconducting oxides $(Tl_{1-x}V_x) Sr_2 (Ca_{0.8}Y_{0.2}) Cu_2O_7$ where x=0.2 and x=0.5 agree well with that expected for such structure. The Tl-O distances were found 2.21 Å and 2.23 Å for these compounds (Table 1). The results lead to the conclusion that the substitution of vanadium at Tl site does not change the local environment around thallium ion. Only one peak was obtained in the Fourier transform of k^3 versus $\chi(k)$ of the Tl L_{III} edge EXAFS of the two superconducting oxides. This peak can be attributed to the oxygen atoms surrounding thallium ion. FT spectra do not show any significant structure above the first coordination shell. The Coordination numbers in both the oxides estimated from curve fitting analysis were almost same and equal to six conforming predictions of XANES analysis. The distances in both oxides are almost same within the uncertainty in the measurements. Their values appear to agree with those in trivalent thallium compounds where Tl is coordinated to six oxygen neighbors e.g. Tl_2O_3.

CONCLUSIONS

On the basis of the absorption spectra of thallium model compounds we have distinguished between the monovalent and trivalent thallium ions in superconducting oxides. The X-ray absorption spectra of $TI_{1-x}V_x$ $Sr_2(Ca_{0.8}$ $Y_{0.2})Cu_2O_7$ show similarity with the spectra of Tl_2O_3 and other trivalent thallium compounds thereby suggesting the presence of Tl^{+++} ions in octahedral configuration in these oxides. The results obtained are in good agreement with those reported by Studer et al [3, 4] and Vijaykrishanan et al [5].

TABLE1. The Tl-O distances and coordination numbers for vanadium doped superconducting oxides of thallium

Sample	N	R(Å)
$(Tl_{0.8}V_{0.2})$ $Sr_2(Ca_{0.8}Y_{0.2})$ Cu_2O_7	5.9	2.21
$(Tl_{0.5}V_{0.5})$ $Sr_2(Ca_{0.8}Y_{0.2})$ Cu_2O_7	6.1	2.23

ACKNOWLEDGMENTS

Authors are thankful to Mr. M. K. Singh for the formatting of the figures. One of the authors (AA) is thankful to MNNIT, Allahabad, India for providing financial assistance for the participation in the conference.

REFERENCES

1. P.A. Lee and G. Beni *Phys. Rev.* **B15**, 2862 (1977).
2. B. K. Teo and P. A. Lee *J. Am. Chem. Soc.* **101**, 2815 (1979).
3. F. Studer, D. Bourgault, C. Martin, R. Retoux, C. Michel, B.Raveau, F.Dartyge and A. Fontains *Physica C* **159**, 609-615, (1989)
4. F. Studer, R. Retoux, C. Martin, C. Michel, B.Raveau, F. Dartyge, A. Fontains and G. Tourlion *Intl. J. Mod. Phys.* **B 3**, 1085-1096, (1989).
5. V. Vijaykrishanan, G. U. Kulkarni and C. N. R. Rao *Mod. Phys. Lett* **B 4**, 45, (1990).

List of Participants

ABNER DE SIERVO
Instituto de Física - Universidade Estadual de
Campinas
Dep. de Física Aplicada
Cid. Universitária Zeferino Vaz
IFGW-DFA
Barão Geraldo
13083970 Campinas SP
Phone: +55 19 35215370
E-mail: asiervo@ifi.unicamp.br
BRAZIL

ADEBUKUNOLA ADESEUN ADEGBENRO
ty-titco investment int ltd
research dept
1,ojelade str,fadeyi,off ikorodu,road,jibowu,lagos
mainland
23401
lagos
Phone: 2348023871159
E-mail: ade_080@yahoo.com
NIGERIA

ADRIANO HENRIQUE BRAGA
ABTLuS LSQ
Rua Pérola 153 Bloco 10, ap. 12
Jd. Santa Esmeralda
13186546 Hortolândia SP
Phone: 19 92101809
E-mail: hbraGa@lnls.br
BRAZIL

ALAN SILVA DE MENEZES
UNICAMP Física Aplicada
Rua Gilberto Pattaro 150 Casa 46
13084375 Campinas SP
Phone: 35215500
E-mail: almez@ifi.unicamp.br
BRAZIL

ALDO FELIX CRAIEVICH
Instituto de Física - Física Aplicada
Caixa Postal 66318
5315970 São Paulo SP
Phone: (11)30916706
Fax: (11)30916749
E-mail: craievich@if.usp.br
BRAZIL

ALEXANDRE PANCOTTI
Unicamp
Física Aplicada/Grupo de Superfícies
Rua Zacharias Queiroz de Nabão 215 Jd. Paulista
13150000 Cosmópolis SP
Phone: 19 35215366
E-mail: pancotti@ifi.unicamp.br
BRAZIL

ALEXEI KUZNETSOV
Inmetro - Dimat
Av. N. S. das Graças 50 Xerem
25250020 Duque de Caxias RJ
Phone: (21)2679-9811
Fax: (21)2679-9108
E-mail: okuznetsov@inmetro.gov.br
BRAZIL

ANA MARIA PERCEBOM
IQ - UNICAMP - Fisico-Quimica
Cons. Joao da Rocha Mattos 304
13843185 Mogi Guacu SP
Phone: (19)81296655
E-mail: quimica_ana@yahoo.com.br
BRAZIL

ANDREW T. S. WEE
National University of Singapore - Physics
2 Science Drive 3, 312
276306 Singapore
Phone: 6565163333
E-mail: phyweets@nus.edu.sg
SINGAPORE

ANTONIO AUGUSTO MALFATTI GASPERINI
UNICAMP/LNLS
Rua Giuseppe Máximo Scolfaro 10000 Guará
13083970 Campinas SP
Phone: +55 19 8166-6466
Fax: +55 19 3512-1004
E-mail: agasperini@lnls.br
BRAZIL

ARMIN HOELL
Helmholtz Zentrum Berlin für Materialien und Energie
Department of Structural Research
Glienicker Strasse 100 Zehlendorf
14109 Berlin
Phone: 0049 30 8062 3181
Fax: 0049 30 8062 3059
E-mail: hoell@helmholtz-berlin.de
GERMANY

ARVIND AGARWAL
MNNIT, INDIA
Department of Physics
Ashok Nagar 171-C/1
ALLAHABAD 211001
ALLAHABAD U.P.
Phone: 915322422246
Fax: 915322445101
E-mail: arvind.aarvind@gmail.com
INDIA

AZEEZ IYANDA SARAFADEEN
ASU TABLE WATER NIGERIA LIMITED
MANAGER
BLOCK 37D WOLF RD/HADEJA RD KANO CITY 30
BADAWA LAYOUT KANO 234
KANO - KANO STATE
Phone: 2347055533303
Fax: 234022317168
E-mail: ronkesgroups@yahoo.co.uk
NIGERIA

AZUCENA MARISOL MUDARRA NAVARRO
Universidad Nacional de la Plata - Física
calle 64, 501
1900 La Plata Buenos Aires
Phone: 0054-221-4246062
E-mail: mudarra@fisica.unlp.edu.ar
ARGENTINA

BAUDELET FRANÇOIS
SOLEIL
av de la PROVIDENCE 13
92160 ANTONY
Phone: 33 1 46687278
E-mail: francois.baudelet@synchrotron-soleil.fr
FRANCE

BEATRIZ DÍAZ MORENO
Instituto Nacional de Pesquisas Espaciais
Laboratório Associado de Sensores
Av. dos Astronautas 1758 Jardim da Granja
12245970 São José dos Campos SP
Phone: 12 39456578
Fax: 12 39456717
E-mail: beatriz@las.inpe.br
BRAZIL

BOUCHET-FABRE
CNRS-CEA
laboratoire Francis-Perrin
CEA saclay, DSM/IRAMIS/SPAM-LFP, bat 522
91191 gif sur yvette
Phone: 33-16908 9788
Fax: 33-16908 1213
E-mail: brigitte.bouchet-fabre@cea.fr
FRANCE

CAIO HENRIQUE LEWENKOPF
ABTLuS / LNLS
Diretoria
Rua Giuseppe Maximo Scolfaro 10000 Guará
13083100 Campinas SP
Phone: 55 19 35121011
Fax: 55 19 35121004
E-mail: clewenkopf@lnls.br
BRAZIL

CARLA AZIMONTE BOTTAN
Laboratório nacional de Luz Síncrotron
FLUORESCENCIA E ABSORÇAO DE RAIOS-X - FAX
Rua Giuseppe Máximo Scolfaro 1000 Bairro Guará
13083100 Campinas SP
Phone: +55 (19) 92 53 41 82
E-mail: carla@lnls.br
BRAZIL

CARLOS ALBERTO PÉREZ
Laboratorio Nacional de Luz Sincrotron
X-Ray Fluorescence and Absorption group
Caixa Postal 6192
Barao Geraldo
13083970 Campinas SP
Phone: +55 19 3512-1043
Fax: +55 19 3512-1004
E-mail: perez@lnls.br
BRAZIL

CARLOS AUGUSTO CARDOSO PASSOS
Universidade Federal Fluminense
Física
v. Gal. Milton Tavares de Souza s/nº. Gragoatá
24210346 Niterói RJ
Rio de Janeiro
Phone: 21 2629 5795
E-mail: cacpassos@yahoo.com
BRAZIL

CARLOS GILES
UNICAMP
IFGW/DFMC
Cidade Universitaria Z. Vaz
13083970 Campinas SP
Phone: 551935215497
Fax: 551935214146
E-mail: giles@ifi.unicamp.br
BRAZIL

CAROLINE ARANTES DA SILVA
Instituto de Química / UFRJ Físico-Química
24020125 Niterói RJ
Phone: (21)91788893
E-mail: arantescarol@yahoo.com.br
BRAZIL

CHRIS BENMORE
Argonne National Laboratory
X-ray Science Division
9700 S. Cass Ave
60439 Argonne IL
Phone: 630 252 4207
Fax: 630 252 5391
E-mail: benmore@aps.anl.gov
UNITED STATES

CHRISTIAN M. SCHLEPÜTZ
Paul Scherrer Institut
Swiss Light Source WBBA
Villigen PSI AG
Phone: +41 56 310 45 36
E-mail: christian.schlepuetz@psi.ch
SWITZERLAND

COLIN NORRIS
Diamond Light Source
Science Division
Diamond House
Harwell Science Campus
OX11 0DE
Didcot
Phone: 331235778045
Fax: 331235778448
E-mail: colin.norris@diamond.ac.uk
UNITED KINGDOM

COTTE
C2RMF - ESRF
rue Ste Colombe 11
94240 L'Hay les Roses
Phone: + 33 1 40 20 57 59
Fax: + 33 4 76 88 27 85
E-mail: cotte@esrf.fr
FRANCE

CRISTIANE BARBIERI RODELLA
Laboratório Nacional de Luz Síncrotron
Laboratório de Síntese Química
Rua Giuseppe Máximo Scolfaro 10000 Guará
13083970 Campinas SP
Phone: +55 19 3512-1010
Fax: +55 19 3512-1004
E-mail: cristiane@lnls.br
BRAZIL

CRISTIANO LUIS PINTO OLIVEIRA
UNIVERSITY OF AARHUS
DEPARTMENT OF CHEMISTRY
LANGELANDSGADE 140
8000 AARHUS JYLLAND
Phone: +45 89 42 38 50
Fax: +45 86 19 61 99
E-mail: CRISLPO@CHEM.AU.DK
DENMARK

DANIEL EDUARDO WEIBEL
UFRGS Físico-Química
Av. Bento Gonçalves 9500 Agranomia
91501970 Porto Alegre RS
Phone: 51-33086204
Fax: 51-33087304
E-mail: danielw@iq.ufrgs.br
BRAZIL

DANIEL REGE CATINI
Universidade Estadual de Campinas
Físico-Química
Rua Pedro Salvato 77 Jardim Flórida
13801061 Mogi Mirim SP
Phone: (19) 91046657
E-mail: g059938@iqm.unicamp.br
BRAZIL

DANIELA COELHO DE OLIVEIRA
LNLS
Laboratório de Síntese Química - LSQ
Rua Giuseppe Maximo Scolfaro 10000 Guará
13083970 Campinas SP
Phone: 19 3512 1040
Fax: 19 3512 1004
E-mail: doliveira@lnls.br
BRAZIL

DANIELA ZANCHET
LNLS Scientific
Guiseppe Maximo Scolfaro 10000
13083970 Campinas SP
E-mail: zanchet@lnls.br
BRAZIL

DENISE APARECIDA TALLARICO DA SILVA
Universidade Federal de São Carlos
Departamento de Engenharia de Materiais
Rua Episcopal 2392 Apto 33
13560570 São Carlos SP
Phone: 55-16-35014784
E-mail: deniseboni@yahoo.com.br
BRAZIL

DOSCH, HELMUT
Max Planck Institute for Metals Research
Dosch
Heisenbergstr. 3
70569 Stuttgart
Phone: -6892562
Fax: -6892564
E-mail: Claudia.Sussdorff@mf.mpg.de
GERMANY

EDSON MASSAYUKI KAKUNO
Universidade Federal do Pampa
R. Carlos Barbosa (unipampa), S/N
B. Getulio Vargas
96412420 Bage RS
Phone: 53-3247-2367
E-mail: edsonmk2004@yahoo.com
BRAZIL

EDUARDO GRANADO
Unicamp IFGW
Cidade Universitária "Zeferino Vaz" S/N
13083970 Campinas SP
Phone: (19) 3521 5444
Fax: (19) 3521 5427
E-mail: granado@lnls.br
BRAZIL

ELIANA NAVARRO DOS SANTOS MUCCILLO
IPEN
Center of Materials Science and Technology
R. do Matão, Trav. R, 400 Cidade Universitária -
Butantã
5508000 São Paulo SP
Phone: 11-31339203
Fax: 11-31339276
E-mail: enavarro@usp.br
BRAZIL

EMMERLING, FRANZISKA
Federal Institut for Materials Research and Testing
(BAM)
X-Ray Structural Analysis
Richard-Willstätter-Str. 11
12489 Berlin
E-mail: franziska.emmerling@bam.de
GERMANY

ERENBURG SIMON
Nikolaev Institute of Inorganic Chemistry SB RAS
Lavrentiev Ave 3
630090 Novosibirsk
Phone: 7-383-3333166
Fax: 7-383-3309489
E-mail: simon@che.nsk.su
RUSSIAN FEDERATION

ERNEST AMOONOO
Practical Emergency Aid Services
Health
Latebu Street East Cantonments 233
box 496 Trade Fair, La Accra - Greater
233 Accra
Kpeshie
Phone: 00233-21-773064
Fax: 00233-21-784117
E-mail: practemaid@yahoo.com
GHANA

EUGENIO OTAL
CITEFA - CINSO
S. J. Bautista LA Salle 4397 VIlla Martelli
1603 Vicente Lopez
Buenos Aires
Phone: +54-11-47098100 ext 1212
Fax: -47098057
E-mail: eugenioh@gmail.com
ARGENTINA

FABIANO BERNARDI
Universidade Federal do Rio Grande do Sul - UFRGS
Departamento de Fisica - Instituto de Fisica
Avenida Bento Gonçalves 9500 Bairro Agronomia
91501970 Porto Alegre RS
Phone: (51) 33086436
Fax: (51) 33087286
E-mail: bernardi@if.ufrgs.br
BRAZIL

FABIO FURLAN FERREIRA
LNLS DRX
Rua Giuseppe Máximo Scolfaro 10000 Guará
13083970 Campinas SP
Phone: 551935121285
Fax: 551935121004
E-mail: furlan@lnls.br
BRAZIL

FELIX G. REQUEJO
CONICET - UNLP
IFLP - INIFTA
Calles 49 y 115
1900 La Plata Buenos Aires
Phone: (+54 221) 425 7430 ext: 144
Fax: (+54 221) 425 4642
E-mail: requejo@fisica.unlp.edu.ar
ARGENTINA

FLANK
SOLEIL Synchrotron
Avenue Saint Laurent 34
bat 2
91400 ORSAY
Phone: 33164469516
E-mail: anne-marie.flank@synchrotron-soleil.fr
FRANCE

FRANCESCO D'ACAPITO
CNR-INFM-OGG
Rue Jules Horowitz 6
38000 Grenoble
Phone: +33 4 7688 2426
Fax: +33 4 7688 2743
E-mail: dacapito@esrf.fr
FRANCE

FRANÇOISE EHRBURGER-DOLLE
CNRS/UJF UMR5588
Laboratoire de Spectrométrie Physique
Avenue de la physique 140
38402 Saint Martin d'Hères
Phone: +33 476 63 58 80
Fax: +33 476 63 54 95
E-mail: fehrburg@spectro.ujf-grenoble.fr
FRANCE

G. BRIAN STEPHENSON
Argonne National Laboratory
Materials Science Division
9700 S. Cass Ave.
60439 Argonne IL
Phone: 630 252 3214
Fax: 630 252 7777
E-mail: stephenson@anl.gov
UNITED STATES

GEORGE SRAJER
Argonne National Laboratory
Advanced Photon Source
S. Cass Ave. 9700 Bldg. 401
60439 Argonne Illinois
Phone: 630-252-6374
E-mail: srajerg@aps.anl.gov
UNITED STATES

GERHARD H. FECHER
Johannes Gutenberg - University
Intitute of inorganic and analytical chemistry
Staudinger Weg 9
55128 Mainz
Phone: ++49 6131 3925613
Fax: ++49 6131 3926267
E-mail: fecher@uni-mainz.de
GERMANY

GILBERTO FERNANDES LOPES FABBRIS
LNLS/UNICAMP
Rua Dr. Antonio Hossri 210 Cidade Universitária
13083370 Campinas SP
Phone: 551932875384
E-mail: gfabbris@lnls.br
BRAZIL

GREGÓRIO COUTO FARIA
Universidade de São Paulo
Instituto de Física de São Carlos
Av. Paulo Pinheiro Werneck 395 Santa Mônica
13561235 São Carlos SP
Phone: 16 34128645
E-mail: gcfaria@ursa.ifsc.usp.br
BRAZIL

GUILLAUME BEUTIER
Diamond Light Source
Harwell Science & Innovation Campus
Diamond Light Source
Chilton
OX11 0DE
Phone: +44 1235 778585
Fax: 441235778448
E-mail: guillaume.beutier@diamond.ac.uk
UNITED KINGDOM

GUILLERMO MANUEL HERRERA PEREZ
Universidad Nacional Autonoma de Mexico
Instituto de Ciencias Nucleares
Miguel E. Schultz 48 San Rafael - Cuauhtemoc
6470 Mexico City
Phone: 52 55 55 66 09 36
E-mail: guillermo.herrera@nucleares.unam.mx
MEXICO

GUILLERMO MANUEL HERRERA PEREZ
Universidad Nacional Autonoma de Mexico
Instituto de Ciencias Nucleares
Miguel E. Schulz 48
19 San Rafael, Cuauhtemoc
6470 Mexico City
Phone: 52 55 55 66 09 36
E-mail: gumahepe@hotmail.com
MEXICO

GUINTHER KELLERMANN
LNLS
X-Ray Diffraction
Rua Giuseppe Máximo Scolfaro 10000 Guará
13083970 Campinas SP
Phone: (19) 3512-1284
E-mail: keller@lnls.br
BRAZIL

GUNAR VINGRE DA SILVA MOTA
UNIFAP Física
Campus Universitário Marco Zero do Equador, Rod.
Juscelino Kubitschek, KM-02 Jardin marco Zero
68902280 Macapa AM
E-mail: gun@unifap.br
BRAZIL

GUSTAVO DE MEDEIROS AZEVEDO
LNLS
Rua Giuseppe Máximo Scolfaro 10000
13083 Campinas SP
Phone: 55 19 3512-1010
Fax: 55 19 3512-1004
E-mail: azevedo@lnls.br
BRAZIL

HAROLDO DE MAYO BERNARDES
Unesp Ilha Solteira - Engenharia Civil
Passeio Palmas 404 Zona Sul
15385000 Ilha Solteira SP
Phone: 551837431208
Fax: 551837431160
E-mail: haroldom@dec.feis.unesp.br
BRAZIL

HARRY WESTFAHL JUNIOR
LNLS Científico
PO BOX 6192
13083970 Campinas SP
Phone: 19-35121034
Fax: 19-35121034
E-mail: westfahl@lnls.br
BRAZIL

HELIO TOLENTINO
Institut Néel, CNRS
Condensed Matter
Avenue des Martyrs 25
BP166
38042 Grenoble
E-mail: helio.tolentino@grenoble.cnrs.fr
FRANCE

HIROTOSHI TERASHITA
LNLS/UNICAMP
PO BOX6192
13084 Campinas SP
E-mail: hterashita@lnls.br
BRAZIL

IAN GENTLE
The University of Queensland
School of Molecular and Microbial Sciences
School of Molecular & Microbial Sciences, The
University of Queensland 68
4072 Brisbane Queensland
Phone: +61 7 3365 4800
E-mail: i.gentle@uq.edu.au
AUSTRALIA

ICHIRO HATTA
Japan Synchrotron Radiation Institute
Industrial Application Division
Kouto 111
6795198 Sayo Hyogo
Phone: -3622
Fax: -1598
E-mail: hatta@spring8.or.jp
JAPAN

INTIKHAB ULFAT
Chalmers University of Technology
Applied Physics
Kemivägen 7A 1950
41296 Göteborg VastraGotaland
E-mail: intikhab@chalmers.se
SWEDEN

IRIS C.L. TORRIANI
LNLS EDX
R, Deusdete M. Gomes, 213 Jd. Novo Barão Geraldo
13084723 Campinas SP
Phone: 55-19-3289-2133
E-mail: torriani@lnls.br
BRAZIL

193

ITIE JEAN-PAUL
Synchrotron SOLEIL
L'Orme des Merisiers, St Aubin BP 48
91192 Gif-sur-Yvette
Phone: 33 1 69 35 96 68
E-mail: jean-paul.itie@synchrotron-soleil.fr
FRANCE

JOHN PARISE
stony Brook
1 Highview Ave
11733 poquott NY
Phone: 1-631-689-9630
Fax: 1-631-689-6272
E-mail: john.parise@sunysb.edu
UNITED STATES

JON OTTO FOSSUM
Norwegian University of Science and Technology
Department of Physics
Hoegskoleringen 5
7491 Trondheim
Phone: 4791139194
Fax: 4773597710
E-mail: jon.fossum@ntnu.no
NORWAY

JOSÉ ANTÔNIO BRUM
Associação Brasileira de Tecnologia de Luz Síncrotron
- Diretoria Geral
Rua Giuseppe Maximo Scolfaro 10000
13083100 Campinas SP
Phone: +55 19 35121011
Fax: +55 19 35121004
E-mail: brum@lnls.br
BRAZIL

JOSÉ BRANT DE CAMPOS
Centro Brasileiro de Pesquisas Físicas APL
Xavier Sigaud Street 150
Urca 22290180 Rio de Janeiro RJ
Phone: +55 21 21417140
E-mail: brant@cbpf.br
BRAZIL

JOSÉ JADSOM SAMPAIO DE FIGUEIREDO
UNICAMP-LNLS
Física Aplicada
Rua Giuseppe Máximo Scolfaro, 10000
P.O.6169
13083970 Campinas SP
Phone: 551935121035
E-mail: jjjsampaf@ifi.unicamp.br
BRAZIL

JOUNG REAL AHN
Sungkyunkwan University
Department of Physics
Cheoncheon-Dong, Jangan-Gu 300
440746 Suwon Gyeonggi-Do
Phone: 82-31-290-5901
Fax: 82-31-290-7055
E-mail: jrahn@skku.edu
KOREA, REPUBLIC OF

JUAN MANUEL CONDE GARRIDO
Facultad de Ingeniería, UBA
Física
Francisco Acuña de Figueroa 1235
1180 Buenos Aires
E-mail: jmcondegarrido@fi.uba.ar
ARGENTINA

JULIANA DA SILVA BERNARDES
Universidade Estadual de Campinas (UNICAMP)
Instituto de Química
José Paulino 1613 Centro apto 104
13023102 Campinas SP
Phone: -551981259848
E-mail: julianab@iqm.unicamp.br
BRAZIL

JULIO CÉSAR DA SILVA
Laboratório Nacional de Luz Síncrotron
ERX / SAXS
Rua Antonio Marques de Oliveira 111 Jd. América,
Barão Geraldo
13084420 Campinas SP
Phone: 55(19)35121115
E-mail: jsilva@lnls.br
BRAZIL

JUNJI MATSUI
Hyogo Science and Technology Association
Hyogo Synchrotron Radiation Nanotechnology
Laboratory
1-490-2, Kouto, Shingu-cho, Tatsuno, Hyogo 679-5185
Phone: -2220
Fax: -2225
E-mail: matsui@cast.jp
JAPAN

KEISUKE KOBAYASHI
National Institute for Materials Science
Beamline Station
1-1-1 Kouto Sayo-cho, Hyogo 6795198
Phone: -4956
Fax: -2738
E-mail: koba_kei@spring8.or.jp
JAPAN

KENJI ISHII
Japan Atomic Energy Agency
Synchrotron Radiation Research Center
1-1-1 Kouto, Sayo-cho , Hyogo 6895148
Phone: -3411
Fax: -1079
E-mail: kenji@spring8.or.jp
JAPAN

KINSLEY OWUSU
PRACTICAL EMERGENCY AID SERVICES
HEALTH
No.47 Latebu Street East Cantonments 233
GREATER ACCRA
WEST AFRICA
Phone: 248973290
Fax: 021-784117
E-mail: owusukinsley@yahoo.com
GHANA

LAGARDE
Synchrotron SOLEIL
Avenue St Laurent 34 bat 2
91400 ORSAY
Phone: 33673362000
E-mail: pierre.lagarde@synchrotron-soleil.fr
FRANCE

LE GODEC
CNRS
rue de Lourmel 140
75013 PARIS
Phone: 33 1 44 27 44 59
Fax: 33 1 44 27 44 69
E-mail: yann.legodec@impmc.jussieu.fr
FRANCE

LETICIA GONCALVES NUNES COELHO
Universidade Federal de Minas Gerais
Departamento de Física
R. Ferreira Penteado 535
13010040 Campinas SP
Phone: 19 33864406
E-mail: lcoelho@fisica.ufmg.br
BRAZIL

LINKE JIAN
National University of Singapore
Singapore Synchrotron Light Source
5 Research Link, NUS 2
117603 Singapore
Phone: (65) 6516 1691
Fax: (65) 6773 6734
E-mail: slsjl@nus.edu.sg
SINGAPORE

LUCIA FERNANDEZ BALLESTER
ESRF
DUBBLE BM26
6 rue Jules Horowitz
38043 Grenoble
E-mail: lufernan@esrf.fr
FRANCE

LUIS GALLEGO MARTINEZ
IPEN CCTM
Av. Prof. Lineu Prestes 2242
Cidade Universitária - USP
5508000 São Paulo SP
Phone: + 55 11 31339222
Fax: + 55 11 31339276
E-mail: lgallego@ipen.br
BRAZIL

MAIRA SILVA FERREIRA
Universidade Estadual de Campinas
Físico-Química
Rua Paschoal Picelli 97 Apt. 17 Barão Geraldo
13084145 Campinas SP
Phone: (19) 3521 3154/ (19) 81214995
E-mail: mairasf@iqm.unicamp.br
BRAZIL

MAKOTO WATANABE
None, retired
317 Sankouporasu Tsubasatosu, 2456 Fujinoki-cho,
Tosu-shi, Saga-ken, Japan 1
8410048 Tosu-shi
Phone: 81-942-83-1648
E-mail: watanabemakoto@163.com
JAPAN

MARIA LIONZO
IQ-UFRGS
Físico-química
Av. Bento Gonçalves 9500
Agronomia
91509900 Porto Alegre RS
Phone: 55 51 33086291
E-mail: marialionzo@yahoo.com.br
BRAZIL

MARINA SOARES LEITE
LNLS MTA
Rua Giuseppe Máximo Scolfaro 10000 Guará
13083970 Campinas SP
Phone: 55 19 3512 1166
Fax: 55 19 3512 1004
E-mail: msl@lnls.br
BRAZIL

MARTINEZ CRIADO GEMA
ESRF
EXP.DIVISION
Rue JULES HOROWITZ 6
38043 GRENOBLE
Phone: 0033 4 76 88 2931
Fax: 0033 476 88 27 85
E-mail: gmartine@esrf.fr
FRANCE

MASAYUKI NAGATA
SPring-8
JASRI
KOUTO 1-1, SAYO-CHO, HYOGO 6795198
Phone: 81-791-58-0954
Fax: 81-791-58-0955
E-mail: nagata-m@spring8.or.jp
JAPAN

MAURO ROVEZZI
CNR-INFM-OGG GILDA CRG
rue Jules Horowitz 6
BP 220
38043 Grenoble
Phone: 33438881984
E-mail: rovezzi@esrf.fr
FRANCE

MAURO VANDERLEI DE AMORIM
FACULDADE POLITÉCNICA DE JUNDIAÍ
ENGENHARIA
Av. Benedito Castilho de Andrade 1007 AP. 44 BL 04
13212070 Jundiaí SP
Phone: (11) 3379 0720
E-mail: maurinhoamorim@uol.com.br
BRAZIL

MINKOOK KIM
Sungkyunkwan University
Physics
300 Cheoncheon-dong, Jangan-gu 31211
440749 Suwon Gyounggi
Phone: 82-31-290-7091
Fax: 82-31-299-6505
E-mail: herald.mk@gmail.com
KOREA, REPUBLIC OF

MOHAMMED BAHOU
Syngapore Synchrotron Light Source
National University of Singapore
5 research Link
117603 Singapore
Phone: 65 6516 1069
Fax: 65 6773 6734
E-mail: slsmb@nus.edu.sg
SINGAPORE

MOHAMMED RABIU SANNI
ASU TABLE WATER NIG LTD
DIRECTOR
BLOCK 37D WOLF RD / HADEJA RD KANO CITY
218
BLOCK 30 BADAWA LAYOUT QUOTERS K
KANO STATE
Phone: 2348053245556
Fax: 234022317168
E-mail: asutablewatergroupsnigltd@yahoo.co.uk
NIGERIA

NIGEL POOLTON
Aberystwyth University
Institute of Mathematics and physics
Aberystwyth University
Institute of mathematics Physics
Penglais Campus
Aberystwyth
Phone: 01970 628625
Fax: 01970 622826
E-mail: ngp@aber.ac.uk
UNITED KINGDOM

NILTON GERALDO DE OLIVEIRA JUNIOR
LNLS LSQ
Maria Bicego 221 Barão Geraldo
13084461 Campinas SP
Phone: (19) 32033082
E-mail: noliveira@lnls.br
BRAZIL

NITIN KUMAR AJSIWAL
PT RAVISHANKAR SHUKLA UNIVERSITY RAIPUR
INDIA
SCHOOL OF STUDIES IN CHEMSITRY
SOS in Chemistry, PT RSU Raipur CG India 10
492010 Raipur CG
Phone: +91 9300686330
Fax: +91 771 2262583
E-mail: nitinkjaiswal@hotmail.com
INDIA

NÁDYA PESCE DA SILVEIRA
UFRGS
Rua Santa Terezinha, 50 / 01
900401080 Porto Alegre
Fax: 33087321
E-mail: nadya@iq.ufrgs.br
BRAZIL

ODEDIRAN SULAIMON ADEBAYO
OBECO INVESTMENT LIMITED
laboratory
isolo road mushin 133
10009 mushin lagos
Phone: 2348032241505
E-mail: aodediran@yahoo.com
NORTHERN MARIANA ISLANDS

OHNO HIDEO
JASRI/SPring-8
Management
1-1-1, Kouto, Sayo-cho,Sayo-gun,HY090
Phone: -1722
Fax: -1723
E-mail: ohno@spring8.or.jp
JAPAN

PAULO ATSUSHI SUZUKI
Universidade de São Paulo - Escola de Engenharia de
Lorena
Departamento de Engenharia de Materiais
Polo Urbo Industrial, gleba AI-6
Caixa Postal 116
12602810 Lorena SP
Phone: (0xx12)31599916
Fax: (0xx12)31533006
E-mail: psuzuki@demar.eel.usp.br
BRAZIL

PRINCE JACOB HAYIBOR
Practical Emergency Aid Services Health
P. O. Box 496 Trade Fair La Accra
233 Greater Accra
West Africa
Phone: 00233-20-8269184
Fax: 00233-21-784117
E-mail: marpolprev@yahoo.com
GHANA

PROFESSOR NEVILLE GREAVES
Aberystwyth University
Institute of Mathematics and Physics
Institute of mathematics and Physics, Aberystwyth
University
Penglais Campus
Aberystwyth
Ceredigion
SY23 3BZ
Phone: 00 44 1970 628625
Fax: 00 44 1970 622826
E-mail: gng@aber.ac.uk
UNITED KINGDOM

QUANG VU VAN
Aberystwyth University
Institute of Mathematics & Physics
Institute of Mathematics & Physics, Aberystwyth
University
Penglais Campus
Aberystwyth
Ceredigion
SY23 3BZ
Phone: 00 44 1970 628625
Fax: 00 44 1970 622826
E-mail: qqv05@aber.ac.uk
UNITED KINGDOM

RAQUEL GIULIAN
Australian National University
Electronic Materials Engineering
Condamine Street 19
unit 13 Turner
2612 Canberra ACT
Phone: 61 2 61250037
Fax: 61 2 6125 0511
E-mail: raquelgiulian@gmail.com
AUSTRALIA

RICHARD WEBER
Materials Development, Inc.
3090 Daniels Court
60004 Arlington Heights IL
E-mail: rweber@matsdev.com
UNITED STATES

RODRIGO GRIBEL LACERDA
Universidade Federal de Minas Gerais
Physics Department
Rua Viçosa, 533 ap. 904 São Pedro
30330160 Belo Horizonte MG
E-mail: rlacerda@fisica.ufmg.br
BRAZIL

ROGERIO PANIAGO
UFMG Physics
Av. Antonio Carlos 6627 Pampulha
30123970 Belo Horizonte MG
Phone: 31-34096619
Fax: 31-34095600
E-mail: rogerio@fisica.ufmg.br
BRAZIL

ROOSEVELT DROPPA JR.
LNLS DRX
Rua Giuseppe Máximo Scolfaro 10000 Guará
13083970 Campinas SP
Phone: +55 (19) 9512-1285
Fax: +55 (19) 9512-1004
E-mail: rdroppa@lnls.br
BRAZIL

ROOSEVELT DROPPA JR.
LNLS DRX
Rua Giuseppe Máximo Scolfaro 10000 Guará
13083970 Campinas SP
Phone: +55 (19) 9512-1285
Fax: +55 (19) 9512-1004
E-mail: rdroppa@lnls.br
BRAZIL

RUDOLF WINTER
Aberystwyth University
Institute of Mathematics and Physics
Institute of Mathematics & Physics, Aberystwyth
University
Penglais Campus
Aberystwyth Ceredigion SY23 3BZ
Phone: 00 44 1970 628625
Fax: 00 44 1970 622826
E-mail: ruw@aber.ac.uk
UNITED KINGDOM

SAMPSON AKINLEYE OLUDARE PANNEAH-AJITERU
UNIVERSITY OF IBADAN
SCIENCES
5, J.F.KENNDY , ASOKORO ABJ, IBA, NIGERIA
ABJ, IBA, NIGERIA
23409 ABJ, IBA ABUJA
Phone: 23427505683
Fax: 23495240946
E-mail: universityofibadan40@gmail.com
NIGERIA

SANS TRESSERAS JUAN ANGEL
ESRF
EXP.DIVISION
RUE JULES HOROWITZ 6
38043 GRENOBLE
Phone: 0033 4 76 88 2346
Fax: 0033 476 88 27 85
E-mail: SANSTRES@ESRF.FR
FRANCE

SHIN-ICHI ADACHI
Photon Factory/KEK
1-1, Oho 1
3050801 Tsukuba
E-mail: shinichi.adachi@kek.jp
JAPAN

SHINJI KOHARA
Japan Synchrotron Radiation Research Institute
Research & Utilization Division
Kouto
111 Sayo, 6795198 Hyogo
Phone: -3518
Fax: -1598
E-mail: kohara@spring8.or.jp
JAPAN

SOLARIN FATA SUNDY
ASU TABLE WATER NIG LTD
REPRNATIVES
BLOCK 37D WOLF RD/ HADEJA RD KANO CITY
30 BADAWA LAYOUT KANO CITY
234
KANO KANO STATE
Phone: 2348034237209
Fax: 234022317168
E-mail: nicolars0010@aol.com
NIGERIA

STEPHEN DOYLE
Forschungszentrum Karlsruhe ISS
Hermann-von-Helmholtz-Platz 1
76344 Eggenstein-Leopoldshafen
Fax: 0049 7247 82 61 72
E-mail: doyle@iss.fzk.de
GERMANY

TAKASHI EURA
SPring-8 Service Co., Ltd
Facility Management
2-23-1, Kouto, Kamigori-cho, Ako-gun, Hyogo, Japan
2231 Kouto Kamigori-cho
6781205 Ako-gun Hyogo
Phone: -2607
Fax: -2598
E-mail: eura@spring8.or.jp
JAPAN

THOMAS SPANGENBERG
Forschungszentrum Karlsruhe ISS
Hermann-von-Helmholtz-Platz
76344 Eggenstein-Leopoldshafen
Phone: 491752282363
E-mail: thomas.spangenberg@iss.fzk.de
GERMANY

TOSHIHIRO OKAJIMA
Kyushu Synchrotron Light Research Center
8-chome, Yayoigaoka
8410005 Tosu Saga
Phone: -5961
Fax: -6040
E-mail: okajima@saga-ls.jp
JAPAN

VALDECI BOSCO DOS SANTOS
Instituto de Física de São Carlos
Departamento de Física e Ciência dos Materiais
AV. Trabalhador São-carlense 400 Centro
13566590 São Carlos SP
Phone: (16)3373 9793
Fax: (16) 3373 9824
E-mail: vbsantos@ifsc.usp.br
BRAZIL

VALERIE BRIOIS
SOLEIL
Samba Beamline
L'Orme des Merisiers 48
BP
Saint Aubin
91192 Gif sur Yvette
Phone: 33169359644
E-mail: briois@synchrotron-soleil.fr
FRANCE

VALMOR ROBERTO MASTELARO
Universidade de São Paulo
Instituto de Física de São Carlos
Av Trabalhador Saocarlense 400 centro
13560970 São Carlos SP
Phone: 16033739828
Fax: 16033739824
E-mail: valmor@if.sc.usp.br
BRAZIL

VICTOR HUGO VITORINO SARMENTO
Institute of Chemistry -UNESP - Araraquara
Physical-Chemistry
R. Francisco Degni s/n
14800165 Araraquara SP
Phone: 55 16 3301 6600 pabx 6778
E-mail: victsarm@iq.unesp.br
BRAZIL

VLADIMIR DMITRIEV
ESRF SNBL
rue J.Horowitz 6
38043 Grenoble Isere
Phone: 33-476882851
Fax: 33-476882694
E-mail: dmitriev@esrf.fr
FRANCE

WENDY FLAVELL
The University of Manchester
The Photon Science Institute
Oxford Rd - Alan Turing Building 139
Manchester
Phone: +44 161 306 4466
Fax: +44 161 275 1001
E-mail: wendy.flavell@manchester.ac.uk
UNITED KINGDOM

WIM BRAS
Netherlands Organisation for Scientific Research
DUBBLE@ESRF
Rue Jules Horowitz 6
38180 Grenoble
Phone: 00-33-476882351
Fax: 00-33-476882412
E-mail: wim.bras@esrf.fr
FRANCE

YOSHIHIRO SAITO
Sumitomo Electric Industries, LTD.
1, Taya-cho, Sakae-ku, Yokohama, 244-8588, Japan
Taya-cho, Sakae-ku
2448588 Yokohama
E-mail: ysaito@sei.co.jp
JAPAN

YOSHINORI KATAYAMA
Japan Atomic Energy Agency
Synchrotron Radiation Research Center
Kouto 1-1
6795148 Sayo-cho Hyogo
E-mail: katayama@spring8.or.jp
JAPAN

YOSHIO WATANABE
JASRI/SPring-8
Industrial Application Division
Kouto 1
6795198, Sayo, HYOGO
E-mail: y.wata@spring8.or.jp
JAPAN

Author Index

A

Abramof, E., 130
Acuña, L. M., 153
Agarwal, A., 185
Aguilar, M. R., 141
Alves, M. C. M., 112
Alves de Souza, E., 135
Antao, S., 41
Araujo, L. L., 45, 55, 125, 132
Arenas-Alatorre, J., 156
Azimonte, C., 130

B

Bahou, M., 66
Barbosa Jr., I., 145
Barrett, M. D., 116
Belmar, F., 37
Benmore, C., 5, 79
Bernardes, J. S., 173
Bernardi, F., 112
bin Mahmood, S., 66, 116
Björck, M., 9
Bley, F., 29, 141
Byrne, A. P., 45, 55

C

Casse, F., 66
Chatwin, C. P., 62
Chavira, E., 34
Cheang-Wong, J. C., 156
Chen, A., 66, 116
Chen, H., 66
Chen, S., 1
Chen, W., 1
Cheng, X., 66
Chi, D., 1
Chilida, J., 16
Chupas, P. J., 41
Clarke, R., 9
Cookson, D. J., 45, 125
Costa, T. C. R., 135
Cotte, M., 16

Crespo-Sosa, A., 156

D

da Silveira, N. P., 127
Dhanak, V., 62
Dhanapaul, A. L., 116
Díaz Moreno, B., 130
Didier, B., 66

E

Ehm, L., 41
Ehrburger-Dolle, F., 29, 141, 180

F

Fantini, M. C. A., 153
Ferreira, F. F., 150
Ferreira, M. J., 168
Figueroa, R., 37
Flank, A.-M., 20
Flavell, W. R., 62
Foran, G. J., 55, 125, 132
Fuentes, R. O., 153

G

Galaev, I. Yu., 141
Gallardo, A., 141
Gao, X., 1
Giulian, R., 45, 55, 125
Gomes Aimoli, C., 176
Gonçalves de Paiva, R., 176
Göttlicher, J., 93
Granado, E., 130
Grätze, M., 62
Greaves, G. N., 51, 71, 98
Gu, P., 66